The Animal World

It may look like a mouse, but this North American pika is not a rodent at all. Find out more on page 119.

Knowledge Quest

The Animal World

Published by
The Reader's Digest Association Limited
London • New York • Sydney • Montreal

Contents

How to use Knowledge Quest

Knowledge Quest: The Animal World is a uniquely interactive reference book that brings you the essential facts and a wealth of wide-ranging information on the animals who share our planet.

Knowledge Quest will make adding to your store of knowledge both interesting and fun. It builds into a highly illustrated reference series, with each volume delivering authoritative facts and many other significant things to know about a particular branch of knowledge.

The Animal World is packed with facts on animals of all kinds – their lives, habitats and relationships, and much more – all contained within the core reference section (pages 39 to 153). If you want to use the book as a straightforward source of information the contents page lists the major topics covered, while the detailed index (starting on page 161) allows you to look up specific animals or subjects. If you simply like to browse, you will find that each fascinating piece of information leads you to discover another, and another, and another . . .

What's so special about Knowledge Quest?
The unique feature of **Knowledge Quest** is the set of quiz questions that can be used as an entertaining way to get into the reference information. With **The Animal World** you can use these to test out what you already know about animals, and to lead you eagerly into finding out more.

How do the questions link to the reference section?
There are 100 quizzes of 10 questions each, which are graded and colour-coded for levels of difficulty (see right). Each question is accompanied by a page number, which is the page in the reference section where you will find both the answer and more information on that subject generally.

The answers to all questions relating to the topic of the spread – which will come from several quizzes – are listed by question number in the far-left column. A number (or sometimes a star) following each answer refers you to the box containing the most relevant additional information elsewhere on the spread. More than one box may be indicated, and sometimes none are especially relevant, in which case an additional detail is given with the answer.

The questions in each quiz lead you to several different pages and topics in the reference section, which is great for finding out more, but is not so convenient if you want to use the quizzes as straightforward quiz rounds. So, for all keen quizmasters, we also list the answers to all the questions in each quiz in the 'Quick answers' section which starts on page 154.

Each question in the quizzes at the front of the book is linked by a page number (given immediately below the question number) to a page in the reference section, where you will find the answer, plus additional information on the subject. In this example, question 27 is linked to page 42.

The answers to all the questions relevant to the overall topic of a reference spread are listed by question number in the left-hand column. Each answer is followed by a box reference showing where more information can be found. Sometimes, instead of a box reference, additional information is given with the answer.

Each box on the rest of the reference spread contains information about an aspect of the overall topic. In this example, the topic of pages 42–43 is 'Migrations and journeys', and box ❼ features information on the Arctic tern's annual migration. Sometimes, more than one box will be relevant to an answer.

From question . . .   to answer . . .   to discovering more

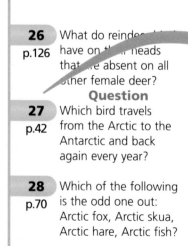

26
p.126
What do reindeer have on their heads that are absent on all other female deer?

Question

27
p.42
Which bird travels from the Arctic to the Antarctic and back again every year?

28
p.70
Which of the following is the odd one out: Arctic fox, Arctic skua, Arctic hare, Arctic fish?

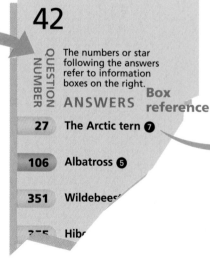

42

QUESTION NUMBER

The numbers or star following the answers refer to information boxes on the right.

ANSWERS   **Box reference**

27   The Arctic tern ❼

106   Albatross ❺

351   Wildebeest

Hib

Pole to Pole ❼

One bird undertakes the **ultimate migration**, flying from the Arctic to the Antarctic and back again every year. The Arctic tern (*Sterna paradisea*, above) breeds inside the Arctic Circle then leaves for the nights arrives

More information

Colour-coding for quizzes of different levels of difficulty

A thousand questions are provided in a hundred themed quizzes. There are three levels of difficulty – **Warm Up**, **In Your Stride** and **Challenge**:

Warm Up quizzes feature easy questions to get you into the swing. Children may enjoy these quizzes as much as adults.

In Your Stride questions are pitched at a more difficult level than 'Warm Up' quizzes, requiring a little more knowledge of the subject.

Challenge quizzes are the most difficult, often requiring in-depth or specialist knowledge. But have a go anyway – you never know what information may be tucked away in the recesses of your brain!

Two other categories, **All Comers** and **Multiple Choice**, include mixed-level questions, ranging from 'warm-up' level to 'challenge', and generally becoming harder as a round progresses.

All Comers quizzes cover a range of levels of questions, from easy to hard. Everyone should be able to join in and see how they get on.

Multiple Choice quizzes offer four possible answers to each question, only one of which is correct. They feature mixed-ability questions, generally arranged to become harder as a quiz progresses.

Special features

Star answers
One answer on each two-page spread is marked with a **star** in the answer column. This indicates a subject of special or unusual interest within the spread topic. (Occasionally, more than one answer in the answers column refers the reader to the star answer box.)

 Aesop

★ 311

Aesop's fables
Aesop is thought to have been born a slave in Greece in the 6th century BC. He is credited

Tie-breaker questions
Some spreads, but not all, feature tie-breaker questions:

Tie-breaker

These questions can be used by quizmasters in a quiz in the event of a tie, but they also contain information that expands on the answer for the interested reader.

Keeping score

The most straightforward **scoring method** is simply to award one point – or if you prefer, two points – for every correct answer.

If you are using the quizzes as rounds in a competition, you may find it easiest to look up the answers in the **Quick Answers** section at the back of the book.

For readers who would like to use this book as an information source for setting quizzes, a blank **Question sheet** and **Answer sheet** are provided at the back of the book. Quizmasters can photocopy the question sheet for their own use, and the answer sheet for distribution among contestants.

Sample quiz
Try out these easy questions to get the hang of it.

1 p.44 Which legless reptiles have forked tongues?

2 p.60 Which rodents use their front teeth for cutting down trees?

3 p.44 On what part of the mouth are most taste buds found?

4 p.144 In the Old Testament of the Bible, who was swallowed by a whale?

5 p.128 Which land-living mammal has the world's largest molars?

6 p.52 What is the term for the sharp teeth of venomous snakes?

7 p.116 Which wriggling creatures are the European mole's favourite food?

8 p.110 What are the long, pointed teeth of carnivores called?

9 p.124 Which sea-living mammal was once hunted for ivory?

10 p.96 Which ferocious sea creatures may grow 24 000 teeth in a lifetime?

True or false?
Decide if these statements about animals are correct.

11 p.104 Ostriches bury their heads in the sand when they are frightened.

12 p.116 Vampire bats drink human blood.

13 p.128 Elephants are afraid of mice.

14 p.88 A starfish that loses an arm will grow back a new one.

15 p.100 Touching a toad can give you warts.

16 p.88 Most slugs and snails are both male and female.

17 p.62 Stone Age people hunted dinosaurs.

18 p.100 Fire salamanders can survive burning.

19 p.140 Cats dropped from height always land on their feet.

20 p.76 Camels store water in their humps.

Pole to pole
Ten questions on polar animals.

21 p.70 Where do polar bears live – in the Arctic or the Antarctic?

22 p.70 Which is larger, the king or emperor penguin?

23 p.70 Which Arctic rodents are famous for their supposedly suicidal migrations?

24 p.122 By what name is the valuable winter fur of the stoat commonly known?

25 p.70 Which large, meat-eating mammal is known by the Inuit as Nanook?

26 p.126 What do reindeer hinds have on their heads that are absent on all other female deer?

27 p.42 Which bird travels from the Arctic to the Antarctic and back again every year?

28 p.70 Which of the following is the odd one out: Arctic fox, Arctic skua, Arctic hare, Arctic fish?

29 p.130 What makes the male narwhal unique among whales?

30 p.70 What do you call the fat that most polar animals have for insulation?

Cats and dogs
Some feline and canine conundrums.

31 p.122 Which animal is descended from the dogs of Australia's first human settlers?

32 p.140 Which tailless breed of cat comes from an island in the Irish Sea?

33 p.120 What sound can the big cats utter that smaller cats cannot?

34 p.146 What breed of dog was the television and film star Lassie?

35 p.58 Which Greek letter identifies the dominant male and female in a wolf pack?

36 p.140 By what name is the Kennel Club's most prestigious dog show commonly known?

37 p.60 What type of wild dog has a burrow called an earth?

38 p.140 Which breed of dog is named after a British monarch?

39 p.140 In what sense did India succeed Socks?

40 p.68 What type of animal was the now-extinct *Smilodon*?

For answers and more facts go to the page given below each question number.
For quick answers to complete quizzes 0 to 6 go to page 154.

Pot luck
A mixed selection of teasers.

41 p.40 What is the world's fastest land animal?

42 p.112 Is the Tasmanian devil a mammal, a reptile or a bird?

43 p.48 Which beetles do battle with antler-like mouthparts?

44 p.150 Which sign of the zodiac is represented by the ram?

45 p.144 What did the legendary Medusa have in place of hair?

46 p.66 Which living sea reptiles survived the event that wiped out the dinosaurs?

47 p.150 What sort of market has bears, stags and bulls?

48 p.86 What type of animal is a sea wasp?

49 p.148 The third track on Bob Marley's album *Natural Mystic* contains the words iron, Zion and what?

50 p.92 Which animals produce gossamer?

High living
Ten questions on animals who live at high altitude.

51 p.78 In which mountain range would you find a vicuña, a condor and a spectacled bear?

52 p.148 What type of creature was the 'Monarch of the Glen', painted by Sir Edwin Landseer?

53 p.78 The ibex is most closely related to which domesticated animal?

54 p.106 Which mountain birds lay their eggs in eyries?

55 p.78 What do the cougar, puma and mountain lion have in common?

56 p.78 By what name is the Himalayan predator the ounce better known?

57 p.78 Bighorn and barbary are both varieties of what type of creature?

58 p.118 Which long-eared animals are pikas most closely related to?

59 p.78 Which Eurasian mountain goat shares its name with a type of soft leather?

60 p.78 The last bucarda died in 2000 in the mountains of which European country?

Deadly serious
Select the correct option from the four possible answers.

61 p.58 What happens to a bee after it stings an intruder?
| A It becomes hungry | B It changes colour |
| C It grows new wings | D It dies |

62 p.52 Hunting by stealth or lying in wait is known as what?
| A Ambling | B Amber |
| C Ambush | D A bush |

63 p.74 Which African wild mammal causes the most human deaths?
| A The aardvark | B The Cape buffalo |
| C The lion | D The wildebeest |

64 p.52 What part of the body does haemotoxic venom affect?
| A The blood | B The lungs |
| C The eyes | D The feet |

65 p.52 Which of the following hunts by using a lure?
| A The anglerfish | B The fishing bat |
| C The gaboon viper | D The baboon |

66 p.54 What does the boxer crab carry to keep predators at bay?
| A Sea anemones | B Starfish |
| C Sea urchins | D Sea slugs |

67 p.52 Which of these is an escape tactic used by antelopes?
| A Lonking | B Pronking |
| C Honking | D Donking |

68 p.90 Which insects transmit sleeping sickness?
| A Tsetse flies | B Midges |
| C Dung flies | D Fleas |

69 p.130 What animal has the Latin name *Orcinus orca*?
| A The death adder | B The deathwatch beetle |
| C The killer bee | D The killer whale |

70 p.102 Which of the following eats the most people every year?
| A Great white shark | B Saltwater crocodile |
| C Tiger shark | D Lion |

Pot luck
A mixed selection of teasers.

71 p.54 — Which armoured South American mammals roll into a ball if threatened?

72 p.112 — In which country would you find a wombat?

73 p.60 — Which long-eared animals live in burrows called warrens?

74 p.40 — What is the world's largest bird?

75 p.140 — Which short-legged breed of dog was awarded titles in ancient China?

76 p.122 — What part of a fox is its brush?

77 p.146 — What type of bird is Harry Potter's friend Hedwig?

78 p.148 — Which stage musical had characters called Macavity, Mungojerrie and Skimbleshanks?

79 p.120 — Which creature has the nickname 'King of Beasts'?

80 p.64 — Which 1970s rock band named themselves after the 'king of the tyrant lizards'?

First letters
The initial letter clues should help you find the answers.

81 p.112 — Which 'k' is an Australian animal that eats only eucalyptus leaves?

82 p.114 — What 's' is a slow-moving, tree-dwelling mammal?

83 p.46 — What 'c' are the colours and patterns used by animals to blend into the background?

84 p.46 — What 'a' describes an animal that is white with pink eyes?

85 p.94 — What 'l' is the largest crustacean found on a menu?

86 p.94 — What 'k' forms vast swarms and is the staple diet of many penguins and whales?

87 p.106 — What 't' is the term for the claw of an owl or bird of prey?

88 p.110 — What 'm' is the name for any animal that feeds its young on milk?

89 p.132 — What 'a' is a Madagascan primate with big ears, black fur and a bushy tail?

90 p.82 — Which 'm' is a large relative of the swordfish prized by sports fishermen?

Small world
A series of questions on minibeasts.

91 p.90 — What type of insect is a scarab?

92 p.58 — Which bees defend the hive – workers or drones?

93 p.90 — In the Bible, which insects arrived in the 'eighth plague'?

94 p.48 — Which have feathery antennae – butterflies or moths?

95 p.44 — What was the name of Buddy Holly's backing group?

96 p.92 — What do female spiders keep in a nidus?

97 p.92 — Which breathing condition can house dust mites aggravate?

98 p.56 — What do head lice, or nits, feed on?

99 p.94 — Which little creatures are sometimes called pill-bugs or gammerzows?

100 p.54 — What type of insects defend themselves with formic acid?

Animal anagrams
Use the clues to unravel the anagrams next to them.

101 p.82 — KNOTPLAN Tiny animals and plants that drift through the ocean.

102 p.44 — SHREWSKI Projecting hairs that enhance the sense of touch.

103 p.88 — TAGIN QUIDS The world's largest invertebrate and favourite food of the sperm whale.

104 p.98 — DISHFOG Small sharks sold by fishmongers as rock salmon.

105 p.74 — RESTTIME Plant-eating insects that live in enormous mounds of baked earth.

106 p.42 — ROASTSLAB Huge seabird mentioned in Samuel Taylor Coleridge's *Rime of the Ancient Mariner*.

107 p.80 — REDSKIPUMP A fish of mangrove swamps and muddy shorelines that spends half of its life out of water.

108 p.112 — ACNEDISH Spiny egg-laying mammals with a fondness for ants.

109 p.68 — BITTERSOIL Extinct animals that lived on the sea floor hundreds of millions of years ago.

110 p.82 — BESTOWRUM Simple animals that grow to huge sizes on deep sea hydrothermal vents, or 'smokers'.

For answers and more facts go to the page given below each question number.
For quick answers to complete quizzes 7 to 13 go to page 154.

On the hoof
Ten questions on hoofed animals.

111
p.144
On what type of creature did Jesus ride into Jerusalem?

112
p.50
What word means child and baby goat?

113
p.126
Which African forest antelope has the same name as a hand drum?

114
p.142
Which misguided knight rode a horse called Rocinante?

115
p.142
And who travelled alongside him on a donkey?

116
p.148
What was the first name of the artist Stubbs, famous for his paintings of horses?

117
p.74
What type of animal is an impala?

118
p.126
What nickname for US currency was inspired by trade in deer skins?

119
p.126
Which two hoofed animals appear in the song *Home on the Range*?

120
p.142
Who promised to make his horse, Incitatus, a Roman consul?

What's in a name?
Some unusual names to puzzle over.

121
p.122
Which American president gave his name to the teddy bear?

122
p.138
What is the correct term for a male goose?

123
p.88
Is the sea hare a mammal, a fish or a mollusc?

124
p.90
By what term are apiarists more commonly known?

125
p.132
In which continent would you find a golden potto and a bush-baby?

126
p.136
What is the literal meaning of the Malay words orang-utan?

127
p.114
Aardvark means 'earth pig' in which African language?

128
p.142
What is the common term for a domesticated polecat?

129
p.118
Which mountain rodent is famous for its soft fur, known by the same name?

130
p.66
What is the literal meaning of the word ichthyosaur?

All creatures great and small
Select the correct option from the four possible answers.

131
p.40
What is the world's largest land animal?

A African bush elephant	B Indian lawn elephant
C Australian tree elephant	D American shrub elephant

132
p.96
What is the world's smallest fish?

A The tadpole	B The minnow
C The dwarf goby	D The stickleback

133
p.100
Which of these creatures is the smallest?

A House sparrow	B Stoat
C Arrow-poison frog	D Raccoon

134
p.40
Which of these is the biggest?

A World's largest mammal	B World's largest fish
C World's largest amphibian	D World's largest worm

135
p.130
Which of these records is not held by the sperm whale?

A Deepest-diving mammal	B World's heaviest brain
C World's biggest eyes	D World's largest predator

136
p.40
For its size, which animal can jump the farthest?

A Flea	B Kangaroo
C Rabbit	D Leopard

137
p.130
What is the world's largest dolphin?

A The spotted dolphin	B The common dolphin
C The Indus river dolphin	D The killer whale

138
p.40
What is the world's heaviest flying bird?

A The wandering albatross	B The kori bustard
C The whooping crane	D The Andean condor

139
p.40
What is the world's second largest animal?

A The great white shark	B The whale shark
C The pilot whale	D The fin whale

140
p.100
What is the world's heaviest frog?

A The giant tree frog	B The paradoxical frog
C The African bullfrog	D The Goliath frog

QUIZ 14 WARM UP

QUIZ 15 IN YOUR STRIDE

QUIZ 16 ALL COMERS

QUIZ 17 CHALLENGE

Odd one out
Pick the odd one out from each of the following lists.

141 p.110 Elephant, gazelle, rabbit, snake.

142 p.104 Ostrich, dingo, emu, wallaby.

143 p.56 Flea, scorpion, tick, louse.

144 p.112 Brown bear, black bear, polar bear, koala bear.

145 p.94 Crab, lobster, beetle, prawn.

146 p.122 Lion, wolf, cheetah, leopard.

147 p.114 Long-nosed armadillo, giant armadillo, hairy armadillo, chainmail armadillo.

148 p.54 Hedgehog, porcupine, sea urchin, slug.

149 p.82 Centipede, sea fan, starfish, octopus.

150 p.132 Rabbits, lemurs, monkeys, apes.

Pot luck
A mixed selection of teasers.

151 p.128 Which animal has the largest ears?

152 p.144 In mythology, which one-horned creature could be tamed only by a virgin?

153 p.56 Does a host live on a parasite or a parasite on a host?

154 p.100 For their size, which amphibians jump the farthest?

155 p.58 Which collective noun links monkeys to boy scouts and soldiers?

156 p.88 By what name is the shiny substance on the inside of seashells commonly known?

157 p.96 What is the world's largest living fish?

158 p.136 What do apes have instead of claws?

159 p.142 Which two animals bred together produce a mule?

160 p.106 How do owls get rid of the bones and fur of their prey?

Feeding time
Questions on diners and their dinners.

161 p.72 What did the dinosaur Allosaurus eat?

162 p.72 Which large Chinese animal lives entirely on bamboo?

163 p.110 What word describes an animal that eats both meat and vegetation?

164 p.148 What animal were Duran Duran 'hungry like' in 1982?

165 p.52 What word means an animal that feeds on carrion, or the leftovers of others?

166 p.74 Which tiny animals make up most of the sloth bear's diet?

167 p.136 Which ape (not a human) hunts other animals for food?

168 p.130 What name is given to the flexible plates that filter-feeding whales use to sieve out their food?

169 p.98 What makes up the bulk of a piscivorous animal's diet?

170 p.52 What do all snakes do with their food that most other animals find difficult?

A question of faith
Creatures from the realms of myth and religion.

171 p.144 In the Bible, what sort of bird brought Noah an olive sprig to signify that the Flood was over?

172 p.144 The Hindu god Ganesh has the head of which animal?

173 p.144 Which large wading bird was considered holy by the ancient Egyptians?

174 p.144 With which bird was Athena, the Greek goddess of wisdom, associated?

175 p.120 What does the name Singh, shared by all male Sikhs, mean?

176 p.66 The largest flying animal ever, *Quetzalcoatlus* was named after a god of which South American people?

177 p.140 The goddess Bastet was represented by which mammal, mummified in huge numbers by the ancient Egyptians?

178 p.144 Which 13th-century Italian became the patron saint of animals?

179 p.144 The Hindu god Hanuman takes the form of which animal?

180 p.144 Which animals are Jains forbidden to eat?

For answers and more facts go to the page given below each question number.
For quick answers to complete quizzes 14 to 18 go to page 154.

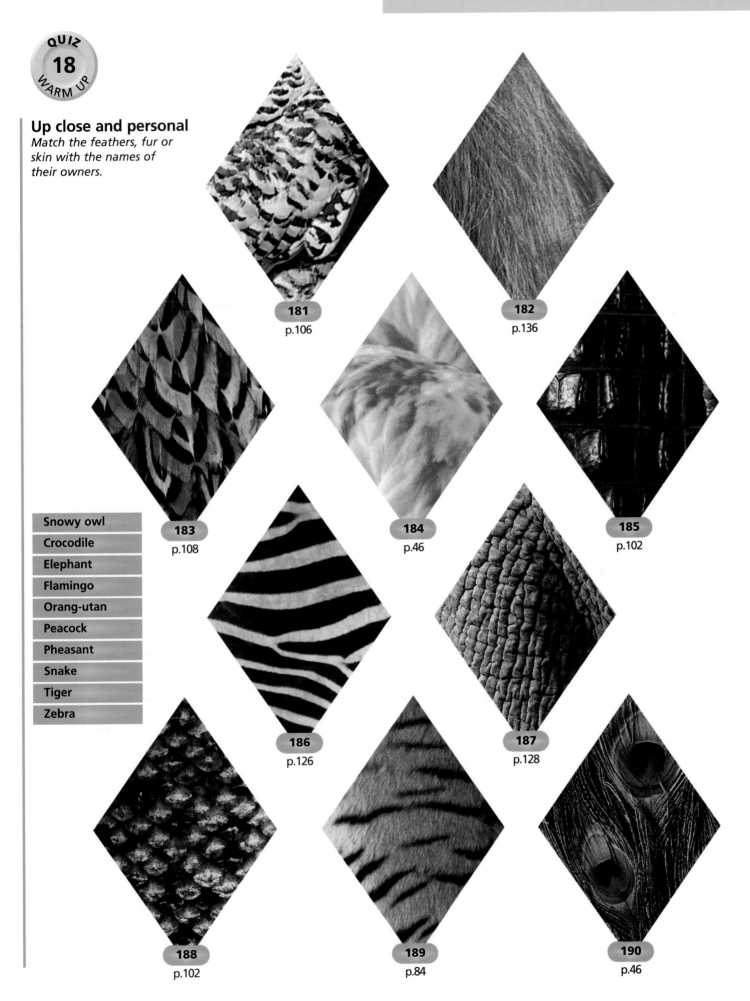

QUIZ
18
WARM UP

Up close and personal
Match the feathers, fur or skin with the names of their owners.

Snowy owl
Crocodile
Elephant
Flamingo
Orang-utan
Peacock
Pheasant
Snake
Tiger
Zebra

181
p.106

182
p.136

183
p.108

184
p.46

185
p.102

186
p.126

187
p.128

188
p.102

189
p.84

190
p.46

Sporting chance
Can you name the animals associated with the sports?

191 p.98 The sport of angling is all about catching what?

192 p.142 Apart from humans, which animals take part in three-day eventing?

193 p.140 Which animals compete using collapsed tunnels and weave poles?

194 p.150 Which swimming stroke is named after an insect?

195 p.142 What animal name is given to the apparatus over which people vault in gymnastics?

196 p.142 Which desert animals are raced outside Al-Ain in the United Arab Emirates?

197 p.150 After which bird of prey is Philadelphia's football team named?

198 p.118 In greyhound racing, the dogs chase a mechanical version of what animal?

199 p.142 Which flying birds compete in races that start together but finish in many different places?

200 p.118 In boxing, what name is given to an illegal punch to the back of the head?

Down on the farm
All these questions are on farmyard animals.

201 p.138 Muscovy and Aylesbury are both breeds of what?

202 p.108 On which continent do turkeys live in the wild?

203 p.138 Name one of the breeds of cow that originated in the Channel Islands.

204 p.138 Pâté de foie gras is made from the liver of which farmyard bird?

205 p.138 From which Southeast Asian country did pot-bellied pigs originate?

206 p.138 What makes the sound 'Kukuriki' in Russia, 'Cocorico' in France, and 'Goockle' in Germany?

207 p.138 Zebu, Highland and Pinzguaer are all breeds of which farm animal?

208 p.142 On which part of a horse's body would you find its fetlocks?

209 p.138 What type of bird is an Indian runner?

210 p.138 Barrows and gilts are both forms of which farm animal?

True or false?
Decide if these statements about animals are correct.

211 p.44 Honey bees dance to tell others where flowers are.

212 p.80 Adult mayflies live for just one day.

213 p.116 Bats are the only mammals that can fly.

214 p.142 Horses sleep while standing up.

215 p.114 The three-toed sloth is the world's slowest mammal.

216 p.110 Mammals include all animals without feathers or scales.

217 p.142 A male donkey is called a jack and a female a jill.

218 p.68 The woolly mammoth was the largest land mammal ever.

219 p.62 Most of the animals that have existed on Earth have now been discovered.

220 p.66 Pterosaurs were flying dinosaurs.

The name game
Ten questions on people who have had animal nicknames.

221 p.150 Which English king was called 'The Lionheart'?

222 p.146 Which Hollywood actor has the nickname 'The Italian Stallion'?

223 p.120 By what nickname is the golfer Eldrick Woods better known?

224 p.90 Stuart Goddard sang *Prince Charming* and *Stand and Deliver* under which assumed name?

225 p.150 Which American golfer is affectionately known as 'The Golden Bear'?

226 p.76 Which Second World War German field marshal was nicknamed 'The Desert Fox?'

227 p.96 By what name is Derek Dick, ex-front man of *Marillion*, better known?

228 p.150 Once among the world's most wanted men, Ilich Ramirez Sanchez was better known as what?

229 p.150 Which Austrian racing driver was nicknamed 'The Clockwork Mouse'?

230 p.148 Which jazz-playing alto saxophonist had the nickname 'Bird'?

For answers and more facts go to the page given below each question number.
For quick answers to complete quizzes 19 to 25 go to pages 154 and 155.

When in Rome...
All these questions have a Latin connection.

231
p.40 The world's fastest bird has the Latin name *Falco peregrinus*. What is its common name?

232
p.120 Which large, majestic carnivore has the Latin name *Panthera leo*?

233
p.144 Romulus, the legendary founder of Rome, was suckled by what type of animal?

234
p.138 Which farm animal has the Latin name *Bos taurus*?

235
p.118 The British band the Stranglers called their first album *Rattus norvegicus*. Which verminous rodent has that Latin name?

236
p.140 Which good friend of man has the Latin name *Canis familiaris*?

237
p.88 Which lettuce-loving mollusc has the Latin name *Helix aspersa*?

238
p.80 Which African mammal has a common name that means 'water horse' in Latin?

239
p.46 Which Italian scooter manufacturer took its name from the Latin for wasp or hornet?

240
p.78 Which hoofed mammals make up the genus *Ovis*?

Pot luck
A mixed selection of teasers.

241
p.144 What type of animal was Ratatosk, who took messages through the World Tree in Norse mythology?

242
p.130 Some whales can jump right out of the water. By what name is this behaviour commonly known?

243
p.132 Are primates' eyes on the side or the front of their heads?

244
p.72 What sort of food does a frugivorous animal eat?

245
p.52 What makes the beaded lizard and gila monster unique?

246
p.114 On which two continents do pangolins live in the wild?

247
p.148 In the 1980s Fatboy Slim was a member of which chart-topping band?

248
p.98 Which Central American country's name means 'many fish' in Spanish?

249
p.48 What three-letter word describes a display ground used by male birds or mammals to attract females?

250
p.46 Which nursery rhyme is all about a melanistic, woolly ruminant?

The natural order
Choose the correct option from the four possible answers to these questions on evolution.

251
p.62 The theory that animals change over time to adapt to their surroundings is known as what?

| A Evocation | B Evolution |
| C Evulsion | D Evisceration |

252
p.62 On which islands was Charles Darwin inspired to come up with this theory?

| A The Galapagos islands | B The Channel islands |
| C The Desert islands | D The Treasure islands |

253
p.62 Where is it thought that life first appeared on our planet?

| A On land | B In the oceans |
| C In rivers | D In the air |

254
p.62 Which of these animal groups appeared on Earth first?

| A Mammals | B Amphibians |
| C Reptiles | D Fish |

255
p.62 Which island animals provided evidence for Darwin's theory?

| A Crocodiles and crows | B Lizards and ostriches |
| C Tortoises and finches | D Snakes and penguins |

256
p.62 After which breed of dog was Darwin's ship named?

| A Bloodhound | B Beagle |
| C Bulldog | D Whippet |

257
p.112 The most primitive living mammals lay eggs. By what name are such mammals known collectively?

| A Monopods | B Monotremes |
| C Monomers | D Marsupials |

258
p.62 Which is not thought to have been one of our ancestors?

| A *Australopithecus* | B *Homo erectus* |
| C *Homo habilis* | D Neanderthal man |

259
p.94 Which of these has barely changed in 150 million years?

| A The horseshoe crab | B The common frog |
| C The cassowary | D The Indian rhinoceros |

260
p.62 Which famous Briton was Charles Darwin's grandfather?

| A Robert Clive | B Josiah Wedgwood |
| C Adam Smith | D Richard Arkwright |

QUIZ 26 WARM UP

Pot luck
A mixed selection of teasers.

261 p.40 What is the world's tallest land animal?

262 p.88 How many feet does a snail have?

263 p.148 Which piano-playing singer released the hit single *Crocodile Rock*?

264 p.100 What steamy habitat do arrow-poison frogs live in?

265 p.146 What type of creature is the cartoon character Roadrunner's enemy?

266 p.104 What type of creatures is an ornithologist interested in?

267 p.54 What do hermit crabs wear on their backs for protection?

268 p.150 In which North American country would you find Great Bear Lake?

269 p.148 What sings 'in the dead of night' on The Beatles' *White Album*?

270 p.144 Which Old Testament prophet escaped from a den of lions?

QUIZ 27 WARM UP

Scrambled seafood
Use the clues to unravel the anagrams next to them.

271 p.98 AUNT Open ocean fish that often associates with dolphins.

272 p.88 CALM Shellfish that often finds its way into chowder.

273 p.98 INADRESS What young pilchards are called, particularly when sold in cans.

274 p.94 NWRAPS These crustaceans are popular in 'cocktails', and are also often found in sandwiches with mayonnaise.

275 p.94 LETSROB A large crustacean with formidable claws.

276 p.88 YESROT Pearl-producing mollusc popular with lovers.

277 p.98 CHOYVAN Salty little fish often used to top pizzas.

278 p.98 ADDHOCK A popular alternative to cod.

279 p.98 ELKCREAM 'Holy' shoaling fish, usually sold smoked.

280 p.98 FHONKISM The name that anglerfish is sold under in restaurants.

QUIZ 28 IN YOUR STRIDE

Animal products
Ten questions relating to animal-derived goods.

281 p.90 Which little creatures produce royal jelly?

282 p.122 Is sable the pelt of a marten, a fox or a deer?

283 p.60 Which Oriental delicacy is made almost entirely from the saliva of cave swiftlets?

284 p.56 Which tiny insects produce honeydew, harvested by ants?

285 p.122 The type of mink farmed for fur coats is native to which continent?

286 p.138 Which hoofed mammal's hair is used to make angora wool?

287 p.138 Which thick, yellow oil is extracted from sheep's wool for cosmetics?

288 p.116 The dung of bats or seabirds, known as guano, is collected for use as what?

289 p.120 What musky substance used in perfume manufacture shares its name with the creature that produces it?

290 p.90 A silkworm is not a worm. What type of animal is it?

QUIZ 29 ALL COMERS

Going places
Modes of travel named after various animals.

291 p.140 The public buses that cross the USA are named after which speedy canine?

292 p.120 Which company built cars called the Mustang and Puma?

293 p.120 Which classic car was redesigned and relaunched by Volkswagen in 2000?

294 p.126 What was the name of the ship in which Sir Francis Drake circled the globe?

295 p.108 The world's fastest ever steam train was named after what type of duck?

296 p.92 Alfa Romeo and Maserati both make cars named after which eight-legged animal?

297 p.108 What was the name of the yacht in which Ellen MacArthur sailed around the world single-handed?

298 p.120 Which British car manufacturer was bought by Ford in 1990?

299 p.66 After which air-breathing sea creature was the world's first submarine named?

300 p.108 The world's biggest ever seaplane was the Hughes Flying Boat. What was its nickname?

For answers and more facts go to the page given below each question number.
For quick answers to complete quizzes 26 to 32 go to page 155.

Stars of page and screen
Animals in film and fiction.

301 p.148 In George Orwell's novel *Animal Farm* what sort of creature was Boxer?

302 p.118 What sort of animals inhabited *Watership Down*?

303 p.146 What type of animal was Pumbaa in Walt Disney's *The Lion King*?

304 p.108 What sort of birds did the Queen of Hearts use for croquet sticks in Lewis Carroll's *Adventures of Alice in Wonderland*?

305 p.146 What was the name of Joy Adamson's feline friend in *Born Free*?

306 p.146 Which 1988 film was based on the life of primatologist Diane Fossey?

307 p.118 In E.B. White's novel *Charlotte's Web*, what type of creature was Templeton?

308 p.146 What type of animal was Clyde in the Clint Eastwood film *Every Which Way But Loose*?

309 p.146 In Jim Henson's television series *The Muppets*, what sort of animal was Robin?

310 p.118 Who was the central character in most of the *Uncle Remus* stories?

Famous names
Answers concern well-known people or their achievements.

311 p.148 Which ancient Greek thinker wrote fables with animal characters?

312 p.146 Which well-travelled zoologist presented *The Blue Planet* and *Trials of Life* on television?

313 p.62 Who wrote *The Origin of Species*?

314 p.136 Jane Goodall made her name studying which African primates?

315 p.66 In the 18th century a Lyme Regis woman called Mary Anning became famous for collecting what?

316 p.148 Who, in 1984, won critical acclaim with a first novel entitled *The Wasp Factory*?

317 p.84 What great feat of organisation was performed by the 18th-century Swede, Carolus Linnaeus?

318 p.140 Which 19th-century poet kept a pet bear while at Trinity College, Cambridge?

319 p.152 Who came up with the Gaia hypothesis that the earth functions as a self-regulating organism?

320 p.152 Which British colonialist and founder of Singapore also founded London Zoo?

Wild blue yonder
Choose the correct option from the four possible answers to these questions with a marine connection.

321 p.82 Deep-sea creatures that emit light are said to be what?

| A Bilious | B Billabongs |
| C Bilingual | D Bioluminescent |

322 p.50 Which of these words is a term for baby fish?

| A Roast | B Boil |
| C Fry | D Sauté |

323 p.124 Which of these seals breed in tropical waters?

| A Fur seals | B Monk seals |
| C Navy seals | D Royal seals |

324 p.82 What percentage of the Earth's surface is covered by water?

| A 35 | B 53 |
| C 71 | D 89 |

325 p.82 Kelp is a type of what?

| A Coral | B Seaweed |
| C Sponge | D Fish |

326 p.82 Tiny animals that drift through the ocean are called what?

| A Primordial soup | B Krill |
| C Zooplankton | D Nekton |

327 p.44 Which of the following is best for communicating over long distances underwater?

| A Colour | B Sound |
| C Scent | D Electricity |

328 p.94 Which of these is not a sea creature?

| A Starfish | B Crayfish |
| C Jellyfish | D Cuttlefish |

329 p.96 Which of these fish are most closely related to sharks?

| A Catfish | B Rays |
| C Eels | D Barracuda |

330 p.82 Pelagic animals are those that live where?

| A In coastal waters | B On the seabed |
| C In the open ocean | D Under rocks |

The flying squad
Ten questions concerning creatures that can fly.

331 p.104 Which American band released an album called *Hotel California*?

332 p.78 Which large, black birds are associated with the Tower of London?

333 p.58 What collective noun can describe a group of birds or a group of sheep?

334 p.148 Which band released the single *Free as a Bird* in 1995?

335 p.112 Is Australia's greater glider a marsupial or a bird?

336 p.56 What plant product do hummingbirds feed on?

337 p.78 Which South American mountain scavenger has the largest wingspan of any bird of prey?

338 p.108 The children's arm of Penguin Books is named after which black and white seabird?

339 p.116 Which flying creatures hunt using a natural form of radar?

340 p.78 Which large bird of prey has a name that means 'lamb catcher' in German?

Four of a kind
Choose the word that best describes all four examples.

341 p.130 Humpback, sei, minke, right.

342 p.110 Incisors, canines, molars, fangs.

343 p.136 Orang-utans, gibbons, gorillas, chimps.

344 p.74 Savannah, prairie, pampas, veldt.

345 p.86 Fire, mushroom, staghorn, brain.

346 p.86 Bell, box, duncecap, moon.

347 p.134 Howler, squirrel, owl-faced, woolly.

348 p.56 Fleas, ticks, hookworms, lice.

349 p.114 Linné's two-toed, pale-throated three-toed, giant ground, maned.

350 p.124 Hooded, bearded, northern fur, grey.

On the move
Anagrams relating to animals and their journeys.

351 p.42 EDIBLESTEW Africa's most famous migrating mammals.

352 p.86 IFSHYJELL Simple animals that spend their adult lives travelling through the sea.

353 p.98 NOALMS Food fish that breeds in fresh water but spends much of its life in the sea.

354 p.124 CASHBEE Where seals and sea lions gather to mate and give birth.

355 p.42 ONEHITBRAIN A relaxing alternative to flying south for the winter.

356 p.42 OWNS EGOSO White waterbird that migrates in huge flocks across North America.

357 p.42 IUCOBRA North American name for migratory Arctic deer.

358 p.42 CONMAID A word describing creatures or people that spend their lives on the move.

359 p.42 MARCHON Regal butterfly that flies to Mexico for the winter.

360 p.42 REGY AWELSH Huge sea mammals that migrate along North America's west coast.

Shelling out
Ten questions on egg-laying creatures.

361 p.104 Which six-letter word means a group of eggs laid at the same time?

362 p.100 The eggs of frogs and toads are commonly called what?

363 p.70 How do emperor penguins prevent their eggs from freezing on the Antarctic ice?

364 p.98 Which 'equine' male fish have a brood pouch for carrying eggs?

365 p.104 Which bird lays an egg that reputedly takes 40 minutes to hard boil?

366 p.100 Do amphibians hatch with lungs or gills?

367 p.104 Which small, flightless bird lays the largest eggs for its size?

368 p.138 To the nearest hundred, how many eggs can a chicken lay in a year?

369 p.112 Two types of mammal lay eggs. Name one of them.

370 p.64 How long was the largest known dinosaur egg: 30 cm (1 ft), 60 cm (2 ft) or 90 cm (3 ft)?

**For answers and more facts go to the page given below each question number.
For quick answers to complete quizzes 33 to 39 go to page 155.**

Pot luck
A mixed selection of teasers.

371 p.58 — What is a group of lions called?

372 p.130 — What type of whale was the albino *Moby Dick*?

373 p.138 — Which European country has the cockerel for its national bird?

374 p.40 — Which insects can leap up to 120 times their own height?

375 p.90 — Which little creatures make up more than two-thirds of all animal species?

376 p.148 — What bird features in the title of US author Harper Lee's only novel?

377 p.142 — What word describes a golden-coloured horse with a pale mane?

378 p.124 — Which have visible ears, seals or sea lions?

379 p.44 — What sense do young deer use to find their mother in a large herd?

380 p.104 — What is the second largest living bird?

Creepy crawlies
A series of questions on minibeasts.

381 p.146 — In which 1986 film did Jeff Goldblum turn into an insect?

382 p.92 — Which deadly black spider has a red spot on its abdomen?

383 p.90 — What does the deathwatch beetle live on?

384 p.52 — Which tropical spiders construct silk-lined burrows with hinged lids?

385 p.148 — Which Norwegian playwright kept a pet scorpion on his desk?

386 p.146 — What did the killer insert into the throats of his victims in *The Silence of the Lambs*?

387 p.90 — Which deadly insects featured in the 1978 film *The Swarm*?

388 p.92 — Australia's most notorious funnel-web spider is named after which of the country's major cities?

389 p.92 — Which pincer-wielding predators carry their young on their backs?

390 p.90 — What sort of insect is a devil's coach-horse?

Scaled from one to ten
Choose the correct option from the four possible answers.

391 p.80 — What is the main food of the gharial or gavial?

A Fish	B Chips
C Turnips	D Yoghurt

392 p.62 — Which island outside the Galapagos has giant tortoises?

A The Isle of Man	B The Isle of Dogs
C Iceland	D Aldabra

393 p.102 — What is the world's longest snake?

A The fat snake	B The verrilong snake
C The reticulated python	D The annapurna

394 p.52 — Which of the following snakes is not venomous?

A The taipan	B The black mamba
C The death adder	D The grass snake

395 p.102 — What is the world's largest living reptile?

A The rhinoceros iguana	B The American alligator
C The leatherback turtle	D The saltwater crocodile

396 p.76 — What habitat does the sidewinder rattlesnake live in?

A Forest	B Heathland
C Prairie	D Desert

397 p.102 — What is the world's largest living lizard?

A The Nile monitor	B The Komodo dragon
C The gila monster	D The basilisk

398 p.80 — What is a caiman?

A A type of crocodile	B A lizard
C A freshwater turtle	D A snake

399 p.102 — What is unusual about viviparous reptiles?

A They are venomous	B They bear live young
C They have no limbs	D They can change colour

400 p.66 — How many living species of marine turtle are there?

A Three	B Eight
C Seventeen	D Twenty-six

True or false?
Decide if these statements about animals are correct.

401 p.110 Dolphins and porpoises are both types of fish.

402 p.48 Some swans keep the same partner for their whole adult lives.

403 p.146 The roadrunner is a real bird.

404 p.110 Only mammals have hair or fur.

405 p.96 A dogfish is a type of small shark.

406 p.112 The red kangaroo is the world's largest marsupial.

407 p.140 The Great Dane was first bred in Denmark.

408 p.90 The glow-worm is not actually a worm.

409 p.76 Bactrian camels have two humps.

410 p.54 Porcupine quills are poisonous.

Pot luck
A mixed selection of teasers.

411 p.138 Which domesticated bird is descended from the red jungle fowl?

412 p.144 In mythology, the griffin was half-eagle, half-what?

413 p.70 Which continent has no native reptiles or amphibians?

414 p.148 Which cat appears in Henri Rousseau's painting *Surprised! Storm in the Forest*?

415 p.90 Woodworms are not worms at all. What sort of animals are they?

416 p.94 By what French name is the Norway lobster familiar to diners?

417 p.142 Which ancient civilisation counted bull-vaulting among its most popular sports?

418 p.92 How does the pill millipede react to danger?

419 p.138 The first cattle to arrive in North America were introduced from which European country?

420 p.108 A female swan is called a pen. What is a male swan called?

Great beginnings
Each answer starts with the word 'great'.

421 p.86 A 1250 mile-long coral deposit off the coast of Queensland.

422 p.106 A British garden bird with white cheeks, a yellow belly and green wings.

423 p.144 The famous mythical beast at Giza with the body of a lion and the head of a man.

424 p.96 The world's biggest predatory fish.

425 p.108 Another name for the loon, a lake-dwelling fish-eater and Canada's national bird.

426 p.106 North America's largest owl, named for its colour.

427 p.122 The constellation Ursa Major, also called the Drinking Gourd and the Big Dipper.

428 p.80 A pond-dwelling beetle large enough to catch small fish.

429 p.108 Diving lake bird found in Eurasia, Africa and Australia named for its flamboyant headgear.

430 p.136 An orang-utan, gorilla or chimpanzee.

Park life
Ten questions connected by a park theme.

431 p.152 London Zoo is located at the northern end of which Royal park?

432 p.152 Which American area of 'natural curiosities' became the world's first national park?

433 p.152 Which national park in southwest England is home to red deer and wild ponies?

434 p.146 Who wrote the book *Jurassic Park* from which the 1993 film was adapted?

435 p.146 What is the first name of the Mr Park who animated Ginger the chicken and the animals of *Creature Comforts*?

436 p.72 Which North American mammal, released into parks in the 19th century, can now be found wild across much of mainland Britain?

437 p.152 Which country contains national parks called RaRa, Royal Bardia and Royal Chitwan?

438 p.152 In which country would you find Kruger National Park?

439 p.126 Which deer were named after a French missionary who first saw them in China's Imperial Hunting Park?

440 p.152 Which Indian national park was named after a famous tiger hunter turned conservationist?

For answers and more facts go to the page given below each question number.
For quick answers to complete quizzes 40 to 44 go to page 156.

Classified images

All of the creatures pictured belong to one of the five groups listed below. Can you work out which group each animal belongs to?

Mammal

Reptile

Amphibian

Fish

Invertebrate

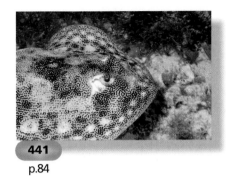

441
p.84

442
p.84

443
p.84

444
p.84

445
p.84

446
p.84

447
p.84

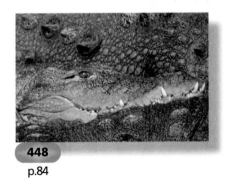

448
p.84

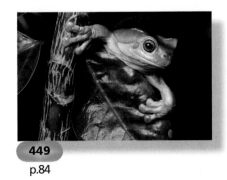

449
p.84

450
p.84

QUIZ 45 WARM UP

Symbols and mascots
Identify the creatures or what they represent.

451 p.72 What is China's national animal?

452 p.106 What is the USA's national bird?

453 p.150 Which bird traditionally symbolises peace?

454 p.120 The prancing horse is the logo of which sports car manufacturer?

455 p.126 What type of animal is Geoffrey, the *Toys 'R' Us* mascot?

456 p.150 Which flying creature appears on the logo for Bacardi rum?

457 p.120 Which big cat appears on Peugeot car badges?

458 p.84 Tony advertises Kellogg's Frosties. What type of animal is he?

459 p.150 Which sun-drenched US city has a football team called the Dolphins?

460 p.150 Which sportswear firm is named after an American cat?

QUIZ 46 IN YOUR STRIDE

All together now
Match each group to its collective noun below.

461 p.58 A group of cows.

462 p.58 A group of dogs.

463 p.58 A group of ducks.

464 p.58 A group of trout.

465 p.58 A group of jellyfish.

466 p.58 A group of starlings.

467 p.58 A group of apes.

468 p.58 A group of crows.

469 p.58 A group of rhinoceroses.

470 p.58 A group of kangaroos.

Crash
Herd
Hover
Mob
Murder
Murmuration
Pack
Raft
Shrewdness
Smack

QUIZ 47 IN YOUR STRIDE

Missing valuables
Fill the gaps with the names of precious substances.

471 p.140 Wild ____fish start life grey and change colour as they grow older.

472 p.102 North America's longest and heaviest poisonous snake is the eastern _____back rattlesnake.

473 p.92 Tiny spiders said to bring good luck if they crawl across your hand are called _____ spiders.

474 p.136 A mature male gorilla is known as a _____back.

475 p.46 The _____ tree boa is a green snake that lives in South American rain forests.

476 p.90 _____fish are primitive insects sometimes found in the home.

477 p.104 The ____crest and firecrest are Europe's two smallest birds.

478 p.56 The ____-throated hummingbird winters in Florida.

479 p.122 The _____-backed jackal is a type of dog found in Africa.

480 p.106 The ____finch is a brightly coloured seed-eating bird.

QUIZ 48 ALL COMERS

Jumbo jumbles
Use the clues to help solve these elephant anagrams.

481 p.128 ORIVY Substance for which elephants are killed by poachers.

482 p.128 KNUTR Flexible extra limb formed from the top lip and nose.

483 p.142 NAILBAHN Carthaginian leader who used elephants to cross the Alps.

484 p.128 SIR KANAL Island where the largest Asian elephants are found.

485 p.128 CHAIRMART The oldest female and leader of an elephant herd.

486 p.128 HERDMYCAP Another word for an elephant, referring to its thick skin.

487 p.128 HADLATIN Country where 'white' elephants are revered.

488 p.128 THUMS Excitable and aggressive physical state entered by bull elephants.

489 p.128 DAMNSOOT An extinct elephant that coexisted with the mammoth.

490 p.128 EXSHARY Small, furry mammals that are elephants' closest land-living relatives.

For answers and more facts go to the page given below each question number.
For quick answers to complete quizzes 45 to 51 go to page 156.

Pot luck
A mixed selection of teasers.

491 p.40 Which 'wandering' seabird has the world's longest wings?

492 p.100 What type of animal is a hellbender?

493 p.42 In which US state are there nearly twice as many caribou as people?

494 p.78 What are the world's only mountain-dwelling wild cattle?

495 p.140 Chihuahua is an area of which Hispanic country?

496 p.64 Which dinosaur's name literally means 'speedy predator'?

497 p.136 Which cartoon band features Blur's Damon Albarn?

498 p.140 Which small household pet is named after a German verb meaning 'to hoard'?

499 p.114 Which sluggish animals had a giant cousin called *Megatherium*?

500 p.106 Two countries have dragons on their national flag. Name one of them.

Fear and loathing
Ten questions on animal phobias.

501 p.92 What is the term for a fear of spiders?

502 p.104 What sort of creatures is an ornithophobic person afraid of?

503 p.118 Musophobia is said to affect elephants but is not a problem for cats. What is it a fear of?

504 p.102 A herpetophobe has a terror of which scaly creatures?

505 p.96 Why do ichthyophobes do their best to avoid watery places?

506 p.116 Which winged night creatures terrified the author Charles Dickens?

507 p.140 James Joyce was cynophobic, which means that he was frightened of what?

508 p.142 Which hoofed mammals do hippophobes have a problem with?

509 p.58 Apiphobia is a fear of insects, but which ones exactly?

510 p.84 What is the word for an irrational fear of all animals?

Out on a limb
Choose the correct option from the four possible answers to these questions on tree-dwellers and forests.

511 p.72 Tails that can grip onto objects are called what?

| A Pretentious | B Prehensile |
| C Prehistoric | D Preposterous |

512 p.132 Lemurs, apes and monkeys are all types of what?

| A Marsupial | B Antelope |
| C Primate | D Carnivore |

513 p.72 Which of these does not live in the rain forest canopy?

| A Howler monkey | B Toucan |
| C Hornbill | D Peccary |

514 p.72 What do woodpeckers eat?

| A Wood | B Leaves |
| C Beetle grubs | D Fungus |

515 p.134 What is the world's smallest monkey?

| A The squirrel monkey | B The spider monkey |
| C The golden lion tamarin | D The pygmy marmoset |

516 p.72 Why do many tree-living animals have binocular vision?

| A To judge distance | B To spot mates |
| C To look for predators | D To see farther |

517 p.72 Where would you expect to find montane rain forest?

| A At sea level | B At high altitude |
| C At high latitude | D Along coasts |

518 p.132 Which of these is the odd one out?

| A The aye-aye | B The indri |
| C The slow loris | D The red squirrel |

519 p.72 Which of these finds most of its food in the branches?

| A Common shrew | B Common dormouse |
| C Bank vole | D Eastern chipmunk |

520 p.114 To which of the following are sloths most closely related?

| A Armadillos | B Monkeys |
| C Rodents | D Pigs |

QUIZ 52 WARM UP

Battle of the sexes
Questions on the male and female of different species.

521
p.52
Among lions, which sex does most of the hunting?

522
p.122
Is a vixen a male or female fox?

523
p.46
Among birds, which sex is usually the more colourful?

524
p.58
What sex are worker ants and bees?

525
p.138
A male sheep is a ram; what is a female sheep called?

526
p.90
Which mosquito bites, the male or female?

527
p.112
Is a boomer a male or female kangaroo?

528
p.48
Which builds the bower, the male or female bowerbird?

529
p.44
Which sex does the singing among crickets and grasshoppers?

530
p.106
In what sport do tiercel and peregrine refer respectively to male and female birds?

QUIZ 53 IN YOUR STRIDE

Food for thought
Identify the foodstuff or where it comes from.

531
p.126
What type of animal does venison come from?

532
p.90
Which substance made by insects is the only food that never spoils?

533
p.138
Which Scottish dish is made from the lungs, heart and liver of a sheep or calf?

534
p.98
Caviar is the salted and seasoned roe of which fish?

535
p.142
Which domesticated Asian animal produces the milk used in the best mozzarella cheese?

536
p.88
By what name is calamari known before it reaches the restaurant?

537
p.144
Jews and Muslims are forbidden to eat the meat of which animal?

538
p.98
Which Greek hors-d'oeuvre is made from the roe of cod or mullet with oil and lemon juice?

539
p.88
Which sea-living molluscs are known by the French as moules?

540
p.88
Are there any shellfish that are actually fish?

QUIZ 54 ALL COMERS

Four of a kind
Choose the word that best describes all four examples.

541
p.70
King, adélie, fairy, rockhopper.

542
p.84
Siberian, Indochinese, Sumatran, Bengal.

543
p.106
Egyptian, griffon, turkey, king.

544
p.42
Waved, black-browed, wandering, sooty.

545
p.64
Coelophysis, Diplodocus, Spinosaurus, Baryonyx.

546
p.108
Canada, snow, greylag, barnacle.

547
p.100
Cane, natterjack, midwife, spadefoot.

548
p.116
Little brown, long-eared, pipistrelle, horseshoe.

549
p.114
Fairy, yellow, giant, nine-banded.

550
p.118
House, long-tailed field, yellow-necked, wood.

QUIZ 55 CHALLENGE

Pot luck
A mixed selection of teasers.

551
p.152
Which word connects the WWF's logo with its UK headquarters?

552
p.116
Which tunnelling mammals give birth in a fortress?

553
p.64
Which modern creatures are thought to be directly descended from dinosaurs?

554
p.90
How many sides does each cell in a honeycomb have?

555
p.102
Which real lizard is named after a mythical monster whose breath and glance were fatal?

556
p.48
What does the male three-spined stickleback build to entice females to lay?

557
p.118
The coypu is an aquatic rodent farmed for its fur. What is its fur called?

558
p.58
Which social insects live in formicaria?

559
p.46
The fire salamander is bold black and yellow. What does this colouring advertise?

560
p.84
Are sea squirts vertebrates or invertebrates?

**For answers and more facts go to the page given below each question number.
For quick answers to complete quizzes 52 to 56 go to page 156.**

QUIZ
56
CHALLENGE

Fishy business
Match the numbers to the labels in the box.

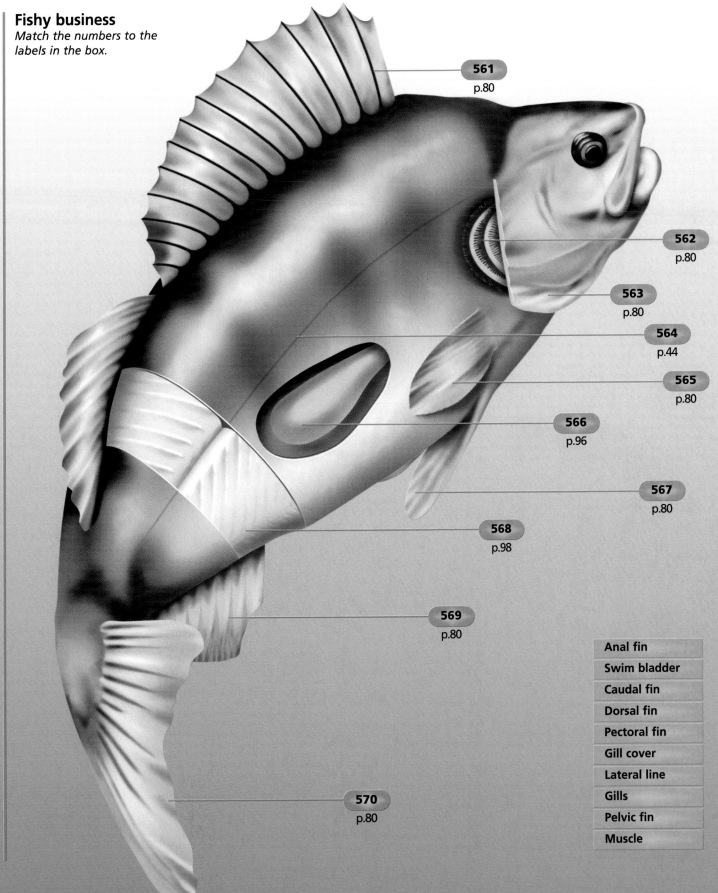

561
p.80

562
p.80

563
p.80

564
p.44

565
p.80

566
p.96

567
p.80

568
p.98

569
p.80

570
p.80

| Anal fin |
| Swim bladder |
| Caudal fin |
| Dorsal fin |
| Pectoral fin |
| Gill cover |
| Lateral line |
| Gills |
| Pelvic fin |
| Muscle |

QUIZ 57 WARM UP

QUIZ 58 WARM UP

QUIZ 59 IN YOUR STRIDE

QUIZ 60 IN YOUR STRIDE

Turn of phrase
Complete each phrase with the correct animal.

571 p.118 To be totally silent is to be as quiet as a _____.

572 p.108 Someone without any hair is as bald as a _____.

573 p.112 To pretend to be dead is to play _____.

574 p.122 A person who does not know when to give up is a _____ for punishment.

575 p.122 To be exceedingly cunning is to be as sly as a _____.

576 p.138 To be in the peak of fitness is to be as strong as an _____.

577 p.140 Something that is really good might be called the _____'s whiskers.

578 p.136 To copy somebody is to _____ their behaviour.

579 p.122 One who seems to be nice but is not is a _____ in sheep's clothing.

580 p.104 Distance measured in a straight line is distance as the _____ flies.

Pot luck
A mixed selection of teasers.

581 p.116 Which animal was 'tamed' in the title of William Shakespeare's fifth play?

582 p.110 How many mammals have feathers?

583 p.136 Do gibbons spend more time on the ground or in trees?

584 p.118 Which are usually larger, rabbits or hares?

585 p.116 What type of animal is a flying fox?

586 p.72 What type of forest is home to the greatest number of species?

587 p.120 Sierra Leone means the mountains of what?

588 p.88 Which oil company has a scallop for its logo?

589 p.48 Which produces clones (exact copies) of the parent, asexual or sexual reproduction?

590 p.136 What type of animal was Ham, one of the first living things in space?

Tail enders
All of the answers end with 'tail'.

591 p.46 A member of a group of butterflies named after a migratory bird.

592 p.142 A horse that has had its tail docked – also the word for mixed alcoholic drinks.

593 p.106 A small, insect-eating bird that moves its tail up and down when it walks.

594 p.104 A fan-shaped joint in carpentry formed by an interlocking tenon and mortise.

595 p.82 A burner producing a broadening jet of flame.

596 p.142 The term for hair tied back in a single bunch.

597 p.138 A popular British soup made from an off-cut of beef.

598 p.118 One of Peter Rabbit's friends in the books of Beatrix Potter.

599 p.142 The horsey name given to wispy cirrus clouds.

600 p.90 A primitive insect that leaps into the air if disturbed.

Altered states
Use the clues to unravel the anagrams next to them.

601 p.46 SOLEMNACHE Lizards that can rapidly alter their colour.

602 p.50 MOTOREMPHASIS The word for a complete change of physical form.

603 p.50 OLDPASTE What baby frogs and toads are known as.

604 p.46 SCARLETAPRIL The term for the larvae of moths and butterflies.

605 p.50 EVILJUNE A word for any animal that has yet to become adult.

606 p.48 ASNOSE What female animals are said to come into when they are ready to breed.

607 p.50 REVELS What eels are known as before they change into their adult form.

608 p.50 TINMOGUL The process of changing feathers or fur.

609 p.50 GHOULSIGN What reptiles are doing when they shed their skin.

610 p.70 GIANTRAMP North European grouse that turns white in winter.

For answers and more facts go to the page given below each question number.
For quick answers to complete quizzes 57 to 63 go to pages 156 and 157.

True or false?
Decide if these statements about animals are correct.

611 p.126 Giraffes give birth while standing up.

612 p.80 The organs that fish use to breathe are called gills.

613 p.86 A flatworm cut in half may grow into two new animals.

614 p.48 The male emperor moth has the best sense of smell in the animal kingdom.

615 p.104 Air passes through a bird's lungs twice with each breath.

616 p.78 Shatoosh shawls are made from the hair of an endangered species of antelope.

617 p.70 The Weddell seal is the world's most southerly mammal.

618 p.62 The first birds appeared on Earth before the first mammals.

619 p.50 Some seabird chicks murder their siblings in the nest.

620 p.116 A shrew's heart beats at about 1200 times a minute.

Monkeying around
Ten questions on apes and monkeys.

621 p.134 What is the male proboscis monkey's most notable feature?

622 p.72 Most monkeys are arboreal. What does arboreal mean?

623 p.134 Gelada, chacma and hamadryas are all varieties of what type of monkey?

624 p.134 How many species of monkey live in the wild in Australia?

625 p.134 What were the three wise monkeys said to see, hear and speak none of?

626 p.134 Why did the residents of the English town of Hartlepool hang a monkey washed ashore there during the Napoleonic Wars?

627 p.134 On which continent would you find tamarins and marmosets living in the wild?

628 p.134 Blood components called Rh factors were discovered during research on which species of macaque?

629 p.134 Apart from its brightly coloured skin, what is the mandrill's main claim to fame?

630 p.134 What aspect of its behaviour makes the douroucouli, or owl monkey, unique?

Hot stuff
Choose the correct option from the four possible answers to these questions on desert-dwellers.

631 p.76 Why do camels have long eyelashes?
| A To keep out sand | B To help them see at night |
| C To flutter at partners | D To make them look nice |

632 p.76 Why do jackrabbits have such big ears?
| A To shade their eyes | B To frighten predators |
| C To listen for prey | D To help them keep cool |

633 p.76 How does the spotted sandgrouse take water to its chicks?
| A In its breast feathers | B In its beak |
| C In its stomach | D On its back |

634 p.76 Which desert antelope was saved from extinction by captive breeding then reintroduced into the wild?
| A The addax | B The springbok |
| C The Arabian oryx | D The scimitar-horned oryx |

635 p.78 Which of these animals does not inhabit deserts?
| A The fennec fox | B The dromedary |
| C The vicuña | D The caracal lynx |

636 p.76 Why does the shovel-nosed lizard have a shovel-like nose?
| A To flip over prey | B To swim through sand |
| C To dig for food | D To attract a mate |

637 p.76 How does the golden mole of the Namib desert find food?
| A By sight | B By smell |
| C By listening for it | D By detecting vibrations |

638 p.76 What type of animal is a jerboa?
| A A lizard | B A rodent |
| C A bird | D A snake |

639 p.76 Which desert is home to wild Bactrian camels?
| A The Sahara | B The Namib |
| C The Gobi | D The Thar |

640 p.118 Which of these desert mammals does not burrow?
| A The jackrabbit | B The kit fox |
| C The kangaroo rat | D The sand cat |

QUIZ 64 WARM UP

Red, white or blue?
Pick the right colour to complete these statements.

641 p.40 The _____ whale is the largest creature on Earth.

642 p.78 The _____ hare occurs in upland areas of Scotland and Wales.

643 p.122 The _____ fox can be found right across the Northern Hemisphere.

644 p.72 The _____ jay inhabits woodlands in eastern North America.

645 p.104 The _____-billed quelea is the world's commonest bird.

646 p.108 The _____ spoonbill feeds on fish and aquatic invertebrates.

647 p.126 The _____ deer is Britain's largest land-living mammal.

648 p.80 The _____ piranha has a reputation for attacking larger animals.

649 p.88 The _____-ringed octopus has a deadly poisonous bite.

650 p.72 The _____ panda lives in mountain forests in southern Asia.

QUIZ 65 IN YOUR STRIDE

Number crunchers
Answer the questions with the correct number.

651 p.88 How many legs does an octopus have?

652 p.90 How many legs do all insects have?

653 p.108 How many pheasants make a brace?

654 p.138 How many blind mice did the farmer's wife chase?

655 p.94 How many pairs of limbs does a decapod have?

656 p.88 How many shells does a snail use in a lifetime?

657 p.92 How many eyes do most spiders have?

658 p.124 How many pups do most seals have in a season?

659 p.128 How many teats does a female elephant have?

660 p.94 How many bones are there inside a barnacle?

QUIZ 66 ALL COMERS

Living quarters
Match the enclosures or homes to their animals.

661 p.96 What is a tank for keeping fish in called?

662 p.140 What is a pet rabbit usually kept in?

663 p.142 What is the word for a building in which horses are housed?

664 p.60 What is the term for a hare's hideout?

665 p.60 What is the word for an otter's riverside burrow?

666 p.104 An enclosure for flying birds is commonly known as a what?

667 p.72 A squirrel's treetop nest is known as a what?

668 p.60 What is the term for a burrow complex dug by badgers?

669 p.60 What is another name for a wasps' nest?

670 p.60 What is the structure in which beavers spend the winter called?

Aquarium
Aviary
Drey
Form
Holt
Hutch
Lodge
Sett
Stable
Vespiary

QUIZ 67 ALL COMERS

Pot luck
A mixed selection of teasers.

671 p.74 Which are larger on average, grassland or forest animals?

672 p.48 Are the Atlas and Spanish Moon types of butterfly or moth?

673 p.110 Are marsupials mammals or birds?

674 p.140 How many breeds of dog does the Kennel Club recognise, to the nearest hundred?

675 p.80 Which close their wings when resting, dragonflies or damselflies?

676 p.128 Which is heavier, an adult male elephant or an adult male elephant seal?

677 p.42 What word means 'to sleep through the winter'?

678 p.42 What word means 'to sleep through the summer'?

679 p.88 In Norse mythology, which relative of the octopus did the kraken resemble?

680 p.136 What is the only animal to have travelled to the Moon?

For answers and more facts go to the page given below each question number.
For quick answers to complete quizzes 64 to 70 go to page 157.

Mixed up mammals
Use the clues to help solve the anagrams next to them.

681 p.116 HESHODEGG Prickly insectivores that roll into a ball when frightened.

682 p.118 PINKCHUM Cute little rodent with stripes running down its back.

683 p.130 IPSOPOSER These look like dolphins but have shorter snouts.

684 p.136 AMHENCEZIP One of the few creatures that uses tools.

685 p.134 SOULCOB An African forest monkey: the best-known type is black and white.

686 p.132 BEHUBBASIS Primitive primates from Africa, also known as galigoes.

687 p.54 INVIARIG SOMOPUS Tree-climbing marsupial native to Canada and the USA, named after a US state.

688 p.124 ALEDROP SALE Spotted sea creature that is the main predator of penguins in Antarctica.

689 p.74 LADEN The world's largest antelope.

690 p.70 BEADWHO The only large whale to spend its whole life in Arctic waters.

Zoo quest
Ten questions on the world's zoos.

691 p.152 The world's largest zoo is outside which city in southern California?

692 p.152 What is unusual about the visiting times of the safari at Singapore Zoo?

693 p.152 In which English zoo would you find the Snowdon Aviary?

694 p.152 Which central Asian zoo had a one-eyed lion that survived a grenade launcher attack in 2001?

695 p.152 Which late author and conservationist founded Jersey Zoo in 1959?

696 p.152 Which Spanish zoo is home to an albino gorilla called Snowflake?

697 p.152 Of what two words is zoo an abbreviation?

698 p.152 Which New York borough contains the city's main zoo?

699 p.152 Which home of dolphins and killer whales has Parks in Florida, Texas and California?

700 p.152 In which southerly city is Australia's oldest zoo?

On the move
Choose the correct option from the four possible answers to these questions about creatures on the move.

701 p.42 Where does the grey whale travel in autumn?
| A From Ireland to Japan | B From the Arctic to Mexico |
| C From Russia to Morocco | D From Australia to Norway |

702 p.42 Where does the European eel go to breed?
| A The Sargasso Sea | B The South China Sea |
| C The Siberian Sea | D The Sea of Tranquillity |

703 p.42 Which antelope migrates across the steppes every year?
| A The sober antelope | B The sombre antelope |
| C The sega antelope | D The saiga antelope |

704 p.50 Which lizards can walk up windows and across ceilings?
| A Chameleons | B Skinks |
| C Iguanas | D Geckoes |

705 p.90 What is the world's fastest-running insect?
| A The American cockroach | B The tiger beetle |
| C The wolf spider | D The army ant |

706 p.40 What is the world's fastest fish?
| A The barracuda | B The nurse shark |
| C The cosmopolitan sailfish | D The flying fish |

707 p.116 How do colugoes travel from tree to tree?
| A They run | B They jump |
| C They glide | D They fly |

708 p.40 Which of these is fastest over long distances?
| A Pronghorn antelope | B Ostrich |
| C Red kangaroo | D Zebra |

709 p.66 How did *Liopleurodon* get from one place to another?
| A It walked | B It swam |
| C It flew | D It slithered |

710 p.72 In which habitat do animals get about by brachiation?
| A Deserts | B Forests |
| C Grasslands | D Mountains |

First letters
Use the initial letters to help you solve these clues.

711 p.124 Elephant, grey and harp are all types of what 's'?

712 p.92 What 't' is a tropical spider that kills mice and birds?

713 p.98 What 'm' is a large eel found on coral reefs in the tropics?

714 p.108 What 'e' is a duck whose feathers are used to fill bedding?

715 p.100 What 'm' is a toad that carries its partner's eggs on its back?

716 p.96 What 's' is a fish with varieties called nurse, bull and mako?

717 p.130 What 'd' is a marine mammal that uses echolocation?

718 p.126 What 'h' is a group formed by animals for protection?

719 p.94 Ghost and fiddler are both types of what 'c'?

720 p.132 What 'n' is the word for animals that are active at night?

Pot luck
A mixed selection of teasers.

721 p.146 What type of animal was Babe, star of the 1995 film of the same name?

722 p.46 Why do some butterflies have spots resembling eyes on their wings?

723 p.56 Greenfly and blackfly are both what type of insect?

724 p.106 The burrowing owl lives on two continents joined by a land bridge. Which two are they?

725 p.52 To which animal does the word leonine refer?

726 p.42 In golf, a score of two under par for a hole is an eagle. What is a score of three under par for a hole called?

727 p.86 What type of sea creature do many people have in the bathroom?

728 p.134 What type of animal is a langur?

729 p.48 Which five-letter word describes a breeding group of females controlled by one male?

730 p.66 What does the word dinosaur actually mean?

Globe trotting
A selection of questions on animals around the globe.

731 p.104 What is New Zealand's national bird?

732 p.136 Which continent do gorillas come from?

733 p.150 Which two creatures appear on Australia's national crest?

734 p.122 With which animal is Russia traditionally associated?

735 p.134 Which small British territory is home to Barbary apes?

736 p.102 On which island would you find the world's largest lizard?

737 p.74 South Africa's rugby team is named after which jumpy animal?

738 p.150 In which landlocked Canadian state are the towns of Beaverlodge, Elk Point and Gibbons?

739 p.106 Which record-breaking scavenger appears on Ecuador's national flag?

740 p.108 Which two African countries have beaches that are home to wild penguins?

Snakes alive!
Ten questions on the theme of snakes.

741 p.52 What is Britain's only venomous snake?

742 p.106 Which country has a rattlesnake on its national flag?

743 p.146 What was the name of the snake in the Disney film of Rudyard Kipling's *The Jungle Book*?

744 p.52 Which continent has the highest proportion of venomous snakes?

745 p.120 Which sports car, made by Dodge, is named after a snake?

746 p.102 Which snakes have a hood that they raise when threatened or agitated?

747 p.150 When was the last Chinese year of the snake: 1995, 1998 or 2001?

748 p.144 Which saint is said to have rid Ireland of its snakes?

749 p.52 How do pythons kill their prey, with poison or by constriction?

750 p.52 In which continent would you find a puff adder and a gaboon viper?

**For answers and more facts go to the page given below each question number.
For quick answers to complete quizzes 71 to 75 go to page 157.**

QUIZ 75 WARM UP

The eyes have it
Who do these eyes belong to? Match the pictures to the list of names below.

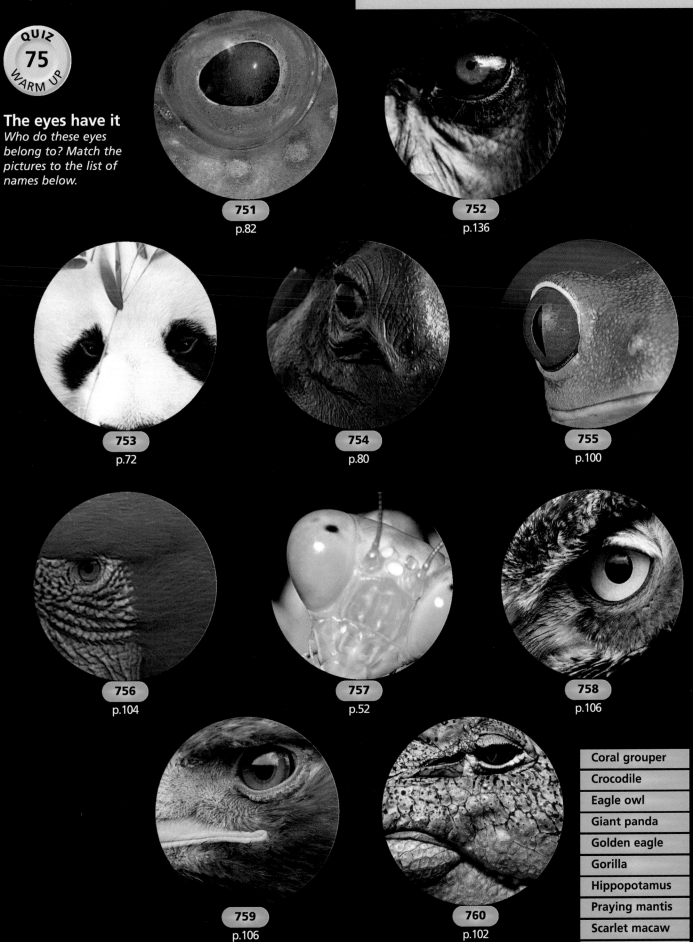

751
p.82

752
p.136

753
p.72

754
p.80

755
p.100

756
p.104

757
p.52

758
p.106

759
p.106

760
p.102

Coral grouper

Crocodile

Eagle owl

Giant panda

Golden eagle

Gorilla

Hippopotamus

Praying mantis

Scarlet macaw

Tree frog

QUIZ 76 WARM UP

Water world
These questions are all on islands or water-dwellers.

761 p.124 Do walruses live in the Northern or Southern Hemisphere?

762 p.80 What do otters, ducks and frogs have between their toes to help them swim?

763 p.80 Lake Baikal is home to the world's only freshwater seal. Where is Lake Baikal?

764 p.150 Which former prison is situated on the Isle of the Pelicans off San Francisco?

765 p.88 Are sea cucumbers plants or animals?

766 p.108 The ancient ceremony of swan-upping occurs every July on which English river?

767 p.82 Does the flashlight fish live on coral reefs or in the deep sea?

768 p.54 Which sea creatures produce clouds of ink to escape from predators?

769 p.82 Which islands, linked with Darwin, are home to the marine iguana?

770 p.86 Which cousins of earthworms are used for blood-letting?

QUIZ 77 IN YOUR STRIDE

Pot luck
A mixed selection of teasers.

771 p.132 Which island is home to all of the world's wild lemurs?

772 p.136 Lar and siamang are varieties of what type of ape?

773 p.128 Does the dugong live on land or in the sea?

774 p.146 Which porky sounding rodent had its 'day' in a 1993 film starring Bill Murray?

775 p.72 Is the spider monkey a grassland or forest animal?

776 p.114 Why does the aardvark have a long, sticky tongue?

777 p.148 Which band had their first UK Number One in 1978 with the single *Rat Trap*?

778 p.116 Are hedgehogs closely related to porcupines?

779 p.112 Which cousin of the koala bear is the world's largest burrowing marsupial?

780 p.116 Which Austrian wrote an operetta named after a bat?

QUIZ 78 IN YOUR STRIDE

True or false?
Decide if these statements about animals are correct.

781 p.106 The dodo was the world's largest pigeon.

782 p.64 Plant-eating dinosaurs ate grass.

783 p.120 All cats can retract their claws apart from the cheetah.

784 p.124 Walruses change colour when they come out of the water.

785 p.116 Most bats can navigate in total darkness.

786 p.130 The sperm whale can dive to depths of more than 2 km.

787 p.52 Hyenas' jaws are strong enough to pulverise bone.

788 p.76 Most desert mammals are active by day.

789 p.68 Some sabretoothed cats had longer teeth than *Tyrannosaurus rex*.

790 p.86 Corals are found only in the tropics.

QUIZ 79 ALL COMERS

Keeping in touch
Unravel these anagrams on animal communications.

791 p.130 HACKBUMP Whale known for its complex, haunting songs.

792 p.44 SKUM Odorous secretion produced by some mammals.

793 p.44 CENTS DANGL Organ from which the above secretion is produced.

794 p.44 TIP REVPI Snake that can 'see' prey simply by sensing its body heat.

795 p.96 MADEHERHAM Shark that picks up electrical activity in muscle to find prey hidden under sand.

796 p.44 NEATANNE Another word for the 'feelers' of crustaceans and insects.

797 p.46 URCOOL Used by many animals to warn that they are poisonous.

798 p.44 EARTALL NILE Sense organ on the bodies of most species of fish.

799 p.48 HOMEPERSON Chemical messengers produced by moths and other animals to attract mates.

800 p.44 ITSRARE Nocturnal Asian primate with huge eyes and ears.

For answers and more facts go to the page given below each question number.
For quick answers to complete quizzes 76 to 82 go to pages 157 and 158.

A question of war
Real or symbolic animal associations with battle.

801
p.84
With which animal are the Tamil Separatists of northern Sri Lanka associated?

802
p.140
Which large breed of dog was used in battle by the Romans?

803
p.106
Which British-made 'jump-jet' is named after a bird of prey?

804
p.76
What was the nickname of Britain's Seventh Armoured Division, who fought in Africa in the Second World War?

805
p.104
Which birds played a vital role in communications in both the First and Second World Wars?

806
p.124
Two types of marine mammal have been trained by the US Navy to seek out mines. Name one of them.

807
p.60
What word describes a pit dug by a soldier for refuge from enemy fire?

808
p.150
The standard borne by an *aquilafer* in the Roman army was topped by the image of which bird?

809
p.70
What are the fur headdresses worn by British soldiers commonly called?

810
p.120
After which tufted-eared cat is the combat helicopter favoured by the Royal Navy named?

All in the name
Do these creatures' names ring a bell with you?

811
p.136
What type of primate is a bonobo?

812
p.52
What sort of reptile is a boomslang?

813
p.106
New Zealand's kea and kakapo are both what type of bird?

814
p.126
Which leaf-eating African mammal is the okapi's closest relative?

815
p.112
In which country do the numbat, koala and spotted cuscus all live?

816
p.132
Is the indri a rodent, a gazelle or a primitive primate?

817
p.114
What type of animal is the insect-eating tamandua from South America?

818
p.122
In which continent would you find a coati, a tayra and a kinkajou?

819
p.74
Literally, what does rhinoceros mean?

820
p.110
Which mammals are grouped into the order Chiroptera?

Prehistoric puzzlers
Choose the correct option from the four possible answers to these questions on prehistoric creatures.

821
p.68
What did the ancient reptile *Dimetrodon* have on its back?

| A A flag | B A curtain |
| C A sail | D An oar |

822
p.64
Which dinosaur was discovered in 1991 near Moab, Utah?

| A *Saltlakeasaurus* | B *Utahraptor* |
| C *Mormonodon* | D *Desertodocus* |

823
p.66
What does the word pterosaur literally mean?

| A Fearful pain | B Earth glider |
| C Winged reptile | D Sea monster |

824
p.68
Ammonites were close relatives of which modern animals?

| A Fish | B Crabs |
| C Squid | D Turtles |

825
p.66
Which of the following was not a dinosaur?

| A *Brachiosaurus* | B *Allosaurus* |
| C *Velociraptor* | D *Plesiosaurus* |

826
p.68
What type of creature was *Argentavis*?

| A A dinosaur | B A mammal |
| C An amphibian | D A bird |

827
p.66
Which of these creatures lived in the sea?

| A *Liopleurodon* | B *Iguanodon* |
| C *Hyracotherium* | D *Pteranodon* |

828
p.64
The smallest dinosaur was the size of a what?

| A Chicken | B Sheep |
| C Cow | D Mouse |

829
p.68
Megalodon would have eaten its terrifying modern equivalent for breakfast. What sort of creature was it?

| A A whale | B A shark |
| C A cat | D A snake |

830
p.64
Which of these is not an Era of geological time?

| A Cenozoic | B Palaeozoic |
| C Anazoic | D Mesozoic |

Black or white?
Fill each gap with the right colour.

831 p.72 The _____ woodpecker is the largest in Europe.

832 p.92 The _____ widow is North America's deadliest spider.

833 p.50 The _____ rhinoceros is the world's heaviest.

834 p.56 The fleas that spread the black death were carried by _____ rats.

835 p.102 The _____ mamba is the world's fastest snake.

836 p.126 The _____-tailed deer causes more traffic accidents than any other US animal.

837 p.46 The _____ panther is a melanistic form of leopard.

838 p.108 The _____ stork is sometimes credited with delivering babies.

839 p.104 The _____ heron shades the water with its wings when hunting for fish.

840 p.122 The _____ bear is North America's third-largest carnivore.

Rearranged rodents
Use the clues to unscramble the anagrams next to them.

841 p.60 EVEBAR Industrious aquatic creature known for building dams.

842 p.58 IREPAIR GOD Type of North American rodent that lives in colonies called towns.

843 p.118 SUREDOOM Famously slept in a teapot in *Alice in Wonderland*.

844 p.118 ARTBIB This long-eared animal is not a rodent but is often confused for one.

845 p.118 PAYACRAB The size of a sheep, this is the world's largest rodent.

846 p.118 EWART LOVE What Ratty from *Wind in the Willows* actually was.

847 p.74 VETRASH SOEMU A tiny European rodent that builds spherical nests in cornfields.

848 p.54 UPPERCOIN A large creature best known for its long protective quills.

849 p.72 RELQUISRS Tree climbing rodents with thick, bushy tails.

850 p.140 ARTMESH A small, tailless rodent often kept as a pet.

Starting with man
All of the answers begin with 'man'.

851 p.128 Vegetarian marine mammals known popularly as sea cows.

852 p.96 Giant plankton-eating ray found in tropical waters.

853 p.108 Perching duck that shares its name with Oriental royalty.

854 p.74 Long-legged dog from the grasslands of South America.

855 p.56 Inflammation of skin in animals, caused by burrowing mites.

856 p.80 Shoreline swamp habitat named after a salt-tolerant tree.

857 p.134 Colourful baboon from the forests of western Africa.

858 p.52 Predatory insect that holds its front legs as if in prayer.

859 p.86 'Portuguese' floating deathtrap with long, trailing tentacles.

860 p.144 Fabulous beast with the head of a man, body of a lion and tail of a dragon or scorpion.

Pot luck
A mixed selection of teasers.

861 p.84 In animal classification which is larger, an order or a family?

862 p.64 What facial features earned the dinosaur *Triceratops* its name?

863 p.132 Lemurs and lorises have a tooth comb. What do they use it for?

864 p.100 What is the scientific study of amphibians and reptiles called?

865 p.148 The symphony *Peter and the Wolf* was written by which Russian composer?

866 p.152 The Audubon Society is primarily concerned with conserving what sort of creatures?

867 p.110 Are seals more closely related to dogs, whales or sea cows?

868 p.126 What is the world's largest species of cattle?

869 p.126 Which is harder to digest, meat or vegetation?

870 p.62 What is unusual about the wings of the chick of South America's hoatzin?

For answers and more facts go to the page given below each question number.
For quick answers to complete quizzes 83 to 87 go to page 158.

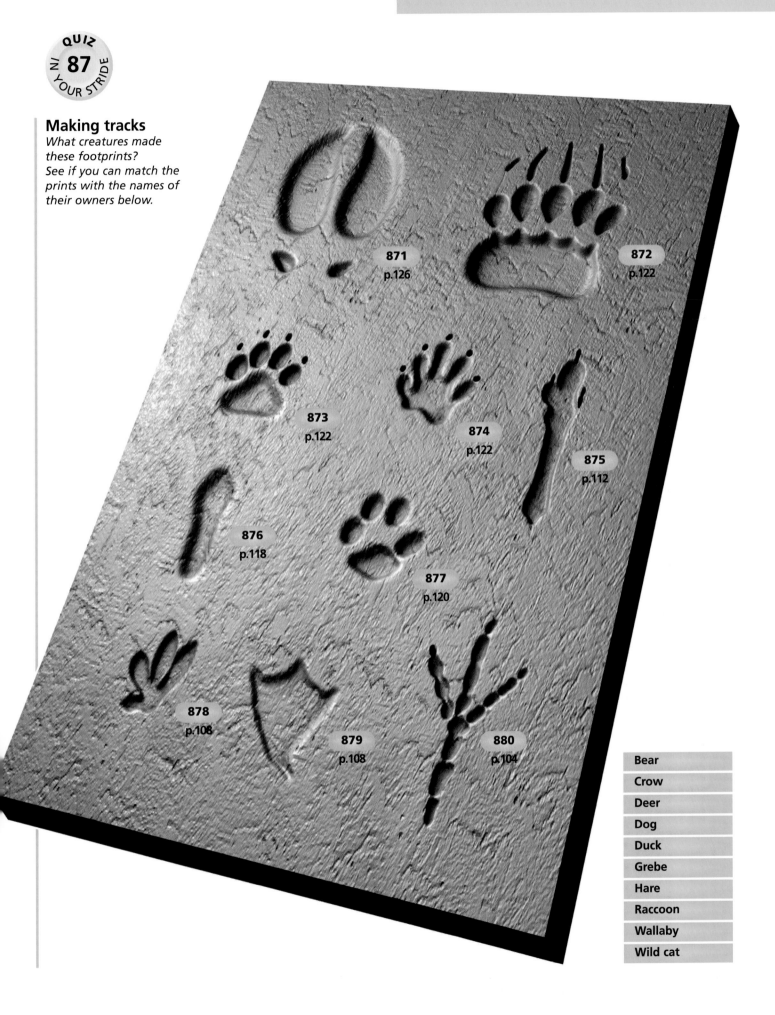

QUIZ 87 IN YOUR STRIDE

Making tracks
What creatures made these footprints?
See if you can match the prints with the names of their owners below.

871 p.126

872 p.122

873 p.122

874 p.122

875 p.112

876 p.118

877 p.120

878 p.108

879 p.108

880 p.104

Bear

Crow

Deer

Dog

Duck

Grebe

Hare

Raccoon

Wallaby

Wild cat

QUIZ 88 WARM UP

Naming babies
Complete the sentences with a word from the list below.

881 p.50 — A young deer is known as a _____.

882 p.50 — A young seal is known as a _____.

883 p.50 — A young cat is known as a _____.

884 p.50 — A young sheep is known as a _____.

885 p.50 — A young crane fly is known as a _____.

886 p.112 — A young kangaroo is known as a _____.

887 p.50 — A young swan is known as a _____.

888 p.50 — A young pigeon is known as a _____.

889 p.50 — A young hare is known as a _____.

890 p.50 — A young bear is known as a _____.

Cub
Cygnet
Fawn
Kitten
Lamb
Leveret
Joey
Leatherjacket
Pup
Squab

QUIZ 89 WARM UP

Pick the biggest
Which is the largest animal in each of these lists?

891 p.120 — Tiger, leopard, puma, jaguar.

892 p.124 — Grey seal, leopard seal, elephant seal, harp seal.

893 p.40 — Ostrich, cassowary, emu, rhea.

894 p.92 — Crab spider, jumping spider, wolf spider, bird-eating spider.

895 p.112 — Grey kangaroo, rock wallaby, wombat, potoroo.

896 p.96 — Sunfish, dogfish, basking shark, lamprey.

897 p.94 — Japanese spider crab, soldier crab, pea crab, box crab.

898 p.56 — Spotted skunk, honey badger, pine marten, stoat.

899 p.114 — Pangolin, pink fairy armadillo, two-toed sloth, giant anteater.

900 p.132 — Mouse lemur, bush-baby, tarsier, indri.

QUIZ 90 IN YOUR STRIDE

First and last
All solutions begin and end with the same letter.

901 p.98 — River fish with brown and rainbow varieties.

902 p.42 — Antlered animals associated with Christmas.

903 p.106 — Large bird of prey, bald in North America and monkey-eating in the Philippines.

904 p.40 — The world's largest boa and heaviest snake.

905 p.70 — Alaskan island, home to the world's largest brown bears.

906 p.50 — The term for a baby goose.

907 p.74 — Continent on which the cheetah and springbok are found.

908 p.130 — South American river, second home of the boto, or Amazon dolphin.

909 p.86 — The name given to an individual coral animal.

910 p.98 — A freshwater fish – the first half of its name is a colour.

QUIZ 91 IN YOUR STRIDE

Common tongue
The Latin name is the clue to the creature in the anagram.

911 p.122 — YECOOT
Canis latrans

912 p.128 — ANAIS THEPLANE
Elephans maximus

913 p.120 — ENDLOG ACT
Felis aurata

914 p.126 — NOMCMO BRAZE
Equus burchelli

915 p.122 — OBNRW BARE
Ursus arctos

916 p.130 — MOCNOM HINDLOP
Delphinus delphis

917 p.70 — RNOBW LIMNGEM
Lemmus lemmus

918 p.54 — ONCOMN ADOT
Bufo bufo

919 p.76 — CABINRAT ELMAC
Camelus bactrianus

920 p.134 — CHINACUP KOYEMN
Cebus capuchinus

For answers and more facts go to the page given below each question number.
For quick answers to complete quizzes 88 to 95 go to page 158.

Odd one out

Pick the odd one out from each of the following lists.

921 p.114　Anteater, aardvark, pangolin, grizzly bear.

922 p.48　Horns, spurs, flippers, antlers.

923 p.46　Wasp, hornet, hoverfly, honeybee.

924 p.124　Fur seal, Weddell seal, pilot whale, walrus.

925 p.110　Milk, fur, molar teeth, scales.

926 p.132　Potto, loris, tarsier, genet.

927 p.130　Sperm whale, humpback whale, fin whale, blue whale.

928 p.94　Robber crab, fiddler crab, edible crab, horseshoe crab.

929 p.56　Leech, flea, tapeworm, tick.

930 p.54　Feathers, poisonous skin, armour, spines.

When dinosaurs ruled

Ten questions on prehistoric creatures.

931 p.64　About how much did the heaviest dinosaur weigh: 10 tonnes, 100 tonnes or 1000 tonnes?

932 p.68　Did ammonites crawl over the seabed or swim in open water?

933 p.146　What type of dinosaur was Aladar, the hero of Disney's animated *Dinosaur* movie?

934 p.64　Which is the most ancient, the Jurassic Period, the Triassic Period or the Cretaceous Period?

935 p.68　*Archaeopteryx* is the most ancient member of which animal group?

936 p.68　Did whales evolve before or after dinosaurs disappeared?

937 p.66　*Ichthyosaurus*, *Rhamphorhynchus* and *Pteranodon* existed at the same time as the dinosaurs but only one lived in the sea. Which one?

938 p.64　Coprolites help scientists understand dinosaur feeding habits. What are coprolites?

939 p.62　How long ago did the dinosaurs disappear: 55, 65 or 75 million years ago?

940 p.64　What was the first dinosaur ever named?

Pot luck

A mixed selection of teasers.

941 p.46　Which flying insects do lepidopterists study?

942 p.140　Adult dogs usually have 10 more teeth than humans – how many is that?

943 p.54　Which part of the body does the spitting cobra fire its venom at?

944 p.76　The horny toad is not a toad at all. What sort of animal is it?

945 p.52　In a food chain, are plant-eating animals primary or secondary consumers?

946 p.48　Which creatures appear in colour in the mostly black and white film *Rumble Fish*?

947 p.64　What title did the dinosaur *Giganotosaurus* steal in 1995?

948 p.86　Tapeworms have no mouths. How do they obtain their food?

949 p.96　What would you find in a mermaid's purse?

950 p.152　What black and white wading bird appears on the logo of the RSPB?

A lesson in Latin

Match the clues to the animals' scientific names.

951 p.120　Wild European cousin of the domestic cat.

952 p.90　Insect whose swarms can devastate crops.

953 p.132　Ring-tailed primate from Madagascar.

954 p.52　A ferocious little insect named after the king of beasts. Digs pitfall traps for ants.

955 p.102　By its common name, this snake sounds like it is good at arithmetic.

956 p.40　A giant that sieves its tiny food from the sea.

957 p.116　A little squeaker – Britain's smallest mammal.

958 p.80　Toothy North American named after the continent's greatest river.

959 p.90　A buzzing creature that calls your house its home.

960 p.84　Deer native to Japan but introduced to Britain and other countries in Europe.

Alligator mississippiensis
Balaenoptera musculus
Cervus nippon
Felis sylvestris
Lemur catta
Locusta migratoria
Musca domestica
Myrmeleon formicarius
Sorex minutus
Vipera berus

QUIZ 96 WARM UP

The sky's the limit
Match the clues to the names of the constellations.

961 p.150 A sign of the zodiac reserved for crabby individuals.

962 p.150 Two fish that herald the start of Spring in the Northern Hemisphere.

963 p.92 A group of stars with a sting in its tail.

964 p.126 Named because it was thought to look like a giraffe.

965 p.150 Zodiac sign named after the King of Beasts.

966 p.102 Has a head and a tail but not much in between.

967 p.58 Something for wolves to howl at when there is no Moon?

968 p.108 Group of stars named after a swan. Also called the Northern Cross.

969 p.142 This constellation's name means 'foal' in Latin.

970 p.130 A streamlined swimmer through the cosmos.

Camelopardalis
Cancer
Cygnus
Delphinus
Equuleus
Leo
Lupus
Pisces
Scorpius
Serpens

QUIZ 97 IN YOUR STRIDE

Pot luck
A mixed selection of teasers.

971 p.78 Is the wallcreeper a reptile or a bird?

972 p.96 Do sharks have skeletons of cartilage or bone?

973 p.86 Which Equator-straddling continent has the world's largest earthworms?

974 p.148 Which 1980s band had a hit with the single *Karma Chameleon*?

975 p.120 A liger is a cross between which two animals?

976 p.60 Which African pig digs a burrow where it shelters at night?

977 p.136 Which continent are orang-utans from?

978 p.148 In the Edward Lear poem, which two creatures went to sea 'in a beautiful pea-green boat'?

979 p.72 South America's largest eagle is named after which female Greek monster?

980 p.150 Which city in New York State has a football team called the Bills?

QUIZ 98 ALL COMERS

True or false?
Decide if these statements about animals are correct.

981 p.54 Skunks' scent can be smelled from over a kilometre away.

982 p.100 Caecilians are legless amphibians.

983 p.116 Bats are the world's second most common mammals.

984 p.110 Musk-oxen can survive temperatures as low as -50°C (-58°F)?

985 p.52 Some snakes spend their whole lives in the sea.

986 p.68 *Basilosaurus* was a dinosaur.

987 p.92 Millipedes have a thousand legs.

988 p.114 The nine-banded armadillo usually gives birth to identical quadruplets.

989 p.102 Crocodiles' stomach juices are so acidic that they can digest skin and bone.

990 p.68 There were mammoths on Earth when the first Pyramids were built.

QUIZ 99 CHALLENGE

Going, going, gone
Ten questions on creatures endangered or extinct.

991 p.106 Which extinct bird's name was derived from the Portuguese word for stupid?

992 p.130 What type of animal is the critically endangered baiji, found only in the Yangtze river?

993 p.138 Before Europe's long-horned aurochs died out in 1627 it gave rise to a familiar farm animal. Which one?

994 p.104 Which American bird plummeted from 9 billion individuals in 1850 to none in 1914?

995 p.152 According to the World Conservation Union (IUCN), which is closer to extinction: a threatened, vulnerable or endangered species?

996 p.112 The thylacine was last spotted in Tasmania in 1961. By what name is this pouched predator better known?

997 p.126 The last quagga died in Amsterdam Zoo in 1883. Which stripy animal did the quagga closely resemble?

998 p.116 Solenodons survive on Haiti, the Dominican Republic and which other island?

999 p.136 How many of the six species of great ape are endangered?

1000 p.128 Steller's sea cow was discovered in the early 1700s. In which century did it become extinct?

For answers and more facts go to the page given below each question number.
For quick answers to complete quizzes 96 to 99 go to page 158.

THE ANIMAL WORLD

Essential facts, figures and
other information on the Animal World

Animal records

Mammals ❶

Largest on Earth	**Blue whale** (*Balaenoptera musculus*): At up to 33.5 m (110 ft) long and weighing up to 200 tonnes, it is the largest animal that has ever existed.
Largest on land	**African bush elephant** (*Loxodonta africana africana*): Males can weigh 12 tonnes and reach 4.2 m (13 ft 10 in) at the shoulder.
Tallest	**Giraffe** (*Giraffa camelopardalis*): Males reach a height of 6 m (20 ft).
Smallest	**Kitti's hog-nosed bat** (*Craseonycteris thonglongyai*): Discovered in Thailand in 1973, it has a head-and-body length of 3.3 cm (1⅓ in) and weighs 2 g (1/16 oz).
Loudest	**Blue whale** and **fin whale** (*Balaenoptera physalus*): Both have been recorded producing sounds of 188 decibels – louder than a space rocket lifting off.
Fastest runner	**Cheetah** (*Acinonyx jubatus*): The **fastest land animal**, it can exceed 96 km/h (60 mph). The distance record-holder is the **pronghorn antelope** (*Antilocapra americana*) which can maintain 88 km/h (55 mph) for 0.8 km (½ mile).
Fastest swimmer	**Killer whale** (*Orcinus orca*) and **Dall's porpoise** (*Phoncoenoides dalli*): Both can reach up to 55 km/h (34 mph) in short bursts.
Longest jumper	**Eastern grey kangaroo** (*Macropus giganteus*): It can clear 13.5 m (45 ft).
Most fertile	**Common tenrec** (*Tenrec ecaudatus*): Each litter may contain up to 31 babies.
Longest lived	Our own species **Homo sapiens**. The world's oldest known person died in 1997 at the age of 122. Next comes **Baird's beaked whale** (*Berardius bairdii*): The oldest recorded individual was 82 years when it was killed in 1975.

TOP CAT The cheetah (left) can accelerate to 96 km/h (60 mph) in just three seconds – faster than any production sports car.

BIG BIRD Southern Africa's kori bustard or paauw (right) is the world's heaviest flying creature.

Birds ❷

Largest	**Ostrich** (*Struthio camelus*): Males grow to 2.75 m (9 ft) tall and 160 kg (350 lb). It is also the **fastest running** bird, capable of 72 km/h (45 mph).
Smallest	**Bee hummingbird** (*Mellisuga helenae*): This tiny Cuban bird measures just 57 mm (2¼ in), including its bill and tail. It weighs just 1.6 g (1/20 oz).
Fastest flier	**Peregrine falcon** (*Falco peregrinus*): When stooping (diving from height) to catch the birds on which it feeds, it can reach more than 200 km/h (124 mph), making it the **fastest animal** of any kind on Earth.
Largest wingspan	**Wandering albatross** (*Diomedea exulans*): This nomadic seabird has the longest wings of any species. Tip to tip they can measure 3.7 m (12 ft).
Heaviest flier	**Kori bustard** (*Ardeotis kori*): At 19 kg (42 lb) it is the heaviest bird capable of flight.
Fastest swimmer	**Gentoo penguin** (*Pygoscelis papua*): It can reach 27 km/h (17 mph) in short bursts.
Longest feathers	**Reeves' pheasant** (*Syrmaticus reevesii*): The male's central tail feathers may reach 2.4 m (8 ft) long, making them the longest feathers of any wild bird.
Longest bill	**Australian pelican** (*Pelicanus conspicillatus*): Its bill grows to 47 cm (18½ in) long.
Most eggs	**Bobwhite quail** (*Colinus virginiatus*): Females may lay up to 28 eggs in a single clutch.

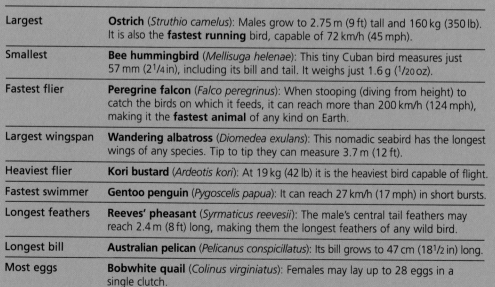

LONG JUMP CHAMPION A human flea (*Pulex irritans*) 2 mm long can jump 33 cm (13 in) – that is 165 times its body length and the equivalent of a man leaping 290 m (950 ft).

33 cm (13 in)

Reptiles

Longest	**Reticulated** (or **giant**) **python** (*Python reticulatus*): Can reach 10 m (33 ft).
Heaviest	**Saltwater crocodile** (*Crocodylus porosus*): Up to 1115 kg (2465 lb).
Shortest	**Jaragua dwarf gecko** (*Sphaerodactylus parthenopion*): Discovered in 2001, it measures just 1.8 cm (7/16 in) from nose to tail.
Most poisonous	*Hydrophis belcheri*: This sea snake produces the most potent venom of any reptile. The **most poisonous land snake** is Australia's fierce snake (*Oxyuranus microlepidotus*).
Most eggs	**Hawksbill turtle** (*Eretmochelys imbricata*): Lays up to 242 eggs at nesting.

❸

HEAVIEST SNAKE South America's anaconda (*Eunectes murinus*) can weigh 225 kg (500 lb) – more than three adult men.

Amphibians

❹

Largest	**Chinese giant salamander** (*Andrias davidianus*): This rare river dweller grows to 1.8 m (5 ft 11 in) long and can weigh 65 kg (143 lb).
Smallest	**Mexican lungless salamander** (*Bolitoglossa mexicana*): Just 2.5 cm (1 in) long.
Most poisonous	**Golden arrow poison frog** (*Phyllobates terribilis*): This species from western Colombia is more than 20 times as poisonous as any other amphibian.
Most eggs	**Cane toad** (*Bufo marinus*): A female lays up to 35 000 eggs per spawning.

QUICK SAIL The 3 m (10 ft) long cosmopolitan sailfish is the fastest animal in water.

❺

Fish

Largest	**Whale shark** (*Rhincodon typus*): Grows up to 18 m (59 ft) and 21 tonnes.
Smallest	**Dwarf goby** (*Trimmatom nanus*): An Indian Ocean fish just 8.8 mm (1/3 in) long.
Most poisonous	**Indian stonefish** (*Synanceia horrida*): This species has the largest venom glands of any fish and is the most deadly to humans.
Fastest swimmer	**Cosmopolitan sailfish** (*Istiophorus platypterus*): Can reach 109 km/h (68 mph).
Most eggs	**Ocean sunfish** (*Mola mola*): Produces over 300 million eggs every time it spawns.

POWERHOUSE For their size, rhinoceros beetles are the world's strongest animals.

❻

Invertebrates

Longest	**Boot-lace worm** (*Lineus longissimus*): A type of ribbon worm from the North Sea, it can grow up to 55 m (180 ft) long, making it the world's longest animal.
Heaviest	**Atlantic giant squid** (*Architeuthis dux*): Frequently exceeds 2 tonnes.
Strongest	**Rhinoceros beetles** (sub-family Dynastinae): Capable of supporting up to 850 times their own bodyweight (compared with 17 times for humans).
Loudest	**Cicadas** (family Cicadidae): Males can be heard from over 400 m (1/4 mile) away.
Smallest	**Mesozoans**: These microscopic parasites consist of just a few cells.
Most fertile	**Cabbage aphid** (*Brevicoryne brassicae*): Females give birth every few hours.
Longest jumper	**Fleas**: For their size, they can jump farther than any other animal.

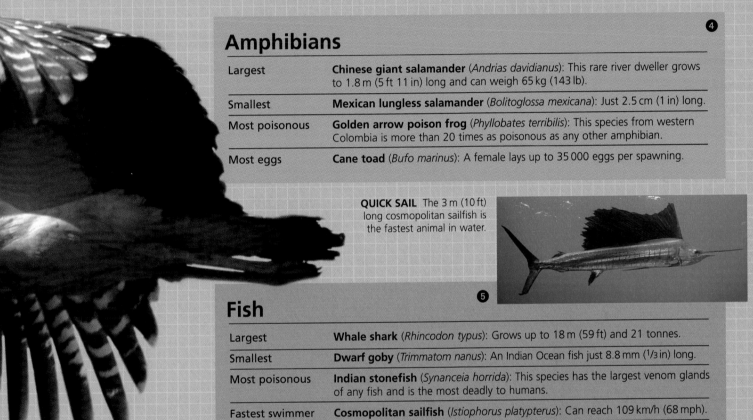

Migrations and journeys

Why animals migrate **1**

◆ Migration allows animals to exploit **seasonal abundances** of food. It also enables them to inhabit places for part of the year where at other times they would not be able to survive.

◆ **Long distance** migration allows creatures to spend their whole lives in an agreeable climate where food is always plentiful. For others it enables them to stock up on food in one place and give birth in another, safer one.

◆ Migration is a **risky** business, however. It is energy expensive and often means negotiating dangerous obstacles, from swollen rivers to large expanses of desert. Animals really only migrate if they have to.

◆ Not all animals that travel actually migrate. Many are simply **nomadic**: they have no fixed home at any time of the year and spend their lives on the move.

To pastures new **2**

The **greatest migrations on land** are those made by grazing mammals. In arctic regions winter forces many animals to move south. Those, such as **caribou**, that eat ground plants have no option but to move as their food source disappears under snow and ice, and temperatures drop to intolerable levels.

Elsewhere the main motivation for grazers to migrate is **drought**. In Africa's Serengeti and Masai Mara vast herds of **wildebeest** leave dry pastures to follow the rains and find new growth. Their annual migration affects the entire savanna ecosystem. **Nile crocodiles** (*Crocodylus niloticus*) that may not feed for the rest of the year gorge themselves as the wildebeest cross the rivers they live in. Other predators such as spotted hyenas (*Crocuta crocuta*) follow the herds, picking off the weakest and sickliest animals.

WEIRD AND WONDERFUL

3 Medieval **theories** of why animals appeared at certain times of the year included the ideas that some birds, such as the turtle dove, hibernated, while others, such as barnacle geese, grew from different creatures entirely.

359

Royal gathering

One of the most spectacular migrations is that of North America's **monarch butterflies** (*Danaus plexippus*). The brightly coloured adults leave Canada and the northern USA in July and fly 2000–3000 km (1250–1850 miles) southwards to winter in Mexico. Migrating monarchs are prone to being blown off course and occasionally end up on the other side of the Atlantic Ocean in Britain or western Europe.

Weight of numbers ❹

The **greatest migration of all** takes place every day **in the sea**. As the sun sinks below the horizon billions of tiny creatures rise up from the depths to feast on the algae near the surface. An estimated 1000 million tonnes of animals make this trip, then return to deeper water with the dawn.

Massive migrations of **individual species** also take place in the oceans but few have ever been properly measured. Mass migrations **on land** and **in the air** are better understood and the largest for which figures are available are listed below.

Animal	Migration route	Additional information
Caribou (reindeer) *Rangifer tarandus*	Tundra to taiga	Caribou move south for winter. About 1.3 million in Canada and Alaska, down from 3 million.
Saiga antelope *Saiga tatarica*	Across the steppes of Kazakhstan	About 2 million saiga overwinter near the north of the Caspian Sea.
Snow goose *Chen caerulescens*	Arctic tundra to south-central USA	Snow geese breed from western Greenland to northeastern Siberia. At least 3 million nest on the Canadian tundra alone.
Swallow *Hirundo rustica*	Northern to Southern Hemisphere	The swallow has an almost global distribution and a worldwide population of tens of millions. Swallows breed in the Northern Hemisphere.
Wilson's storm petrel *Oceanites oceanicus*	Indian, Pacific and Atlantic oceans to Southern Ocean	The world's most abundant seabird. More than 100 million gather on Antarctic and sub-Antarctic islands to breed.

ON THE MOVE More than 1.6 million wildebeest migrate across Africa's plains every year.

Perpetual motion ❺

Nomadic animals make the **greatest journeys of all**, as they never stop moving. Large nomads, such as oceanic dolphins, may cover tens of thousands of kilometres in a lifetime. The world's greatest travellers are the nomadic birds. The common swift (*Apus apus*) spends its life on the wing and clocks up over 500 000 km (310 000 miles) between fledging and landing two years later to breed. The wandering albatross (*Diomedea exulans*) also covers vast distances between breeding seasons.

ALWAYS EAST The wandering albatross rides the roaring forties.

Underwater marathons ❻

The words 'migrating mammal' conjure up images of caribou and wildebeest, but in fact the **longest mammal migrations** are those made by whales. Of all the whales, grey whales (*Eschrichtius robustus*) travel the farthest. Every autumn they swim from the Arctic Ocean down to the west coast of Mexico to calf and breed.

Many fish also travel long distances. Young Atlantic salmon (*Salmo salar*, left) migrate to the middle of the Atlantic to mature, while European eels (*Anguilla anguilla*) swim right across it to breed in the Sargasso Sea.

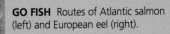

GO FISH Routes of Atlantic salmon (left) and European eel (right).

Pole to Pole ❼

One bird undertakes the **ultimate migration**, flying from the Arctic to the Antarctic and back again every year. The Arctic tern (*Sterna paradisea*, above) breeds inside the Arctic Circle in summer, then leaves for the Antarctic as the nights start to close in. The tern feeds as it travels and arrives in the Antarctic at the height of the southern hemisphere's summer. As a result it spends more of its life in daylight than any other animal.

Arctic terns are just 36 cm (14 in) long, yet each may travel more than 35 000 km (21 750 miles) every year.

HEADING SOUTH One leg of the Arctic tern's epic annual journey.

Senses and communication

Why have senses?

◆ An animal's senses enable it to **move safely** and give it the information that it needs to **find food and a mate**.
◆ Most animals have at least four of the **five main senses**; vision, hearing, smell, taste and touch.

◆ Some animals have extra senses that we find hard to imagine, including the ability to detect changes in electrical activity.
◆ Senses **enable** animals **to communicate**. The more developed a sense is in a species, the more likely it is to be used for communication.

BLANK LOOK This young chimpanzee is relaxed.   **FEAR GRIN** Indicates submission.

In touch ❷

Touch is most highly developed in animals that are active or live **in darkness**. It is often enhanced by whiskers or barbels, which extend the area that can be sensed around an animal's head. Whiskers are unlike most hairs in that they can actually be moved by some creatures at will. Cats, for instance, can manoeuvre their whiskers to detect the size of gaps between objects in total darkness. Touch is also used more than any other sense to reassure.

 794

Heat seekers

Pit vipers, such as North America's **rattlesnakes**, have two heat-sensitive pits, one positioned between each eye and nostril. The pits enable the snakes to detect warm-blooded prey in darkness, when their victims cannot see them coming.

Smell

◆ Scent is the **primary sense among mammals**. Most mammals can smell danger or prey long before they can see or hear it.
◆ In **amphibians**, **reptiles** and **birds** smell is less developed. Petrels (a group of seabirds which include the fulmar, *Fulmaris glacialis*) use it to find carrion in the open ocean, but for most species in these classes it plays a secondary role to vision and hearing.
◆ Many **fish** have an extremely fine-tuned sense of smell. The most sensitive noses of all fish belong to sharks. They can detect one part of blood in a million parts of water, enabling them to home in on injured prey from over 0.5 km (1/3 mile) away.
◆ A few animals use smell to find their way around. The incredible homing act of salmon from the ocean to the rivers where they hatched is a case in point. The fish follow a trail of recognisable scent to the mouth of their home river, which they then swim up to spawn.

FIXED STARES Tarsiers are nocturnal but still find their way by vision. Their eyes are so big they cannot move them.

Seen through different eyes ❹

Vision is important to virtually all animals. For hunters it is vital to be able to spot and follow prey, while for plant-eaters it is just as important to be able to see predators coming. Almost all animals have eyes, even those with no ears or sense of smell. The **simplest eyes** are those of creatures such as flatworms, which can only tell light from dark. At the other extreme, mantis shrimps have the **best colour vision** in the animal kingdom. Their eyes have 10 pigments, compared with our own total of just three.

PANT HOOT Used when calling other groups.

TEETH BARED Communicates aggression and rage.

Can animals talk? ❺

Most animals communicate on a very basic level, producing sights, smells or sounds that tell others about their location and physical condition and little else. But a few can communicate more abstract information, such as how they feel or where something out of sight is located. The ability to do this can be considered **language**. Apes communicate their moods with facial expressions, and chimps can learn sign language that actually lets them communicate with us.

Honeybees have their own form of language. Bees 'dance' to tell others where flowers are, and how much nectar they contain.

Hearing ❻

◆ Like smell, hearing is highly developed in mammals. It is particularly important for **nocturnal hunters** and the animals that they prey upon.
◆ Many mammals can hear sounds that are beyond the range of our ears. **Elephants**, for instance, send messages over long distances with deep rumbles of infrasound, while **bats** use high frequencies to detect insect prey.
◆ Sound is used by male birds and mammals to advertise **territory ownership** and **attract mates**, and plays a large part in deciding whether or not animals will fight – longer or more powerful vocalisations are made by stronger individuals.

Communication ❼

Animals use sight, sound and smell to communicate. **Body language** transfers information instantly and is used to attract mates, intimidate rivals, and avoid conflict. Wolves give **visual signals** with their tails, for example. A raised tail signals dominance while one held between the legs indicates submission.

Sound has the advantage of travelling over long distances, particularly under water. Dolphins use sound to keep in touch when they are too far apart to see each other, and whales produce noises that can travel for hundreds of miles. The low frequency pulses produced by blue whales have been detected from 850 km (530 miles) away.

Scent can carry complex information about an animal's physical condition and has the advantage of lasting over time. A scent mark left one day – perhaps at the boundary of an animal's territory – can still be read and understood by another individual several days later.

SUMMER SINGER Male grasshoppers (below) and crickets rub their legs against their wings to create sound to attract mates. Grasshoppers' ears are on their back legs near the 'knee'.

46

QUESTION NUMBER

The numbers or star following the answers refer to information boxes on the right.

ANSWERS

83 Camouflage ❹

84 Albino ❻

184 Flamingo ❷

190 Peacock – only males have these feathers ⭐

239 Vespa ❸

250 Baa Baa Black Sheep ❻

475 Emerald (the emerald tree boa) ❻

⭐ **523** The male ⭐

559 That it is poisonous ❶

591 Swallowtail ❸

601 Chameleons ❹ ❻

604 Caterpillars ❸

722 To frighten predators ❸

797 Colour ❶

837 Black (the black panther) ❻

923 Hoverfly (it has no sting) ❸

941 Butterflies ❸

Camouflage and display

Colour and pattern ❶

Animals use colour in many ways. Some employ it to **attract a partner**, others to **keep out of sight**. For a few, being bright is the best way to avoid being eaten. Poisonous animals and those with stings advertise the fact that they are dangerous. Many, such as hornets (*Vespa crabro*), combine colour with striking patterns. Yellow and black stripes are a common **signal for danger** in the animal kingdom. Stripes are also used for **camouflage** and to break up an individual's outline in a herd.

Generally speaking, nocturnal animals are less colourful than those that are active by day. Most animals, including ourselves, can see only in black and white after nightfall.

WEIRD AND WONDERFUL ❷

Flamingoes are pink because some brine shrimps they eat are full of pink pigment. If the pink shrimps disappear from the birds' diet, then so does the birds' spectacular colour.

Pretending to be bad ❸

Looking like a more harmful animal is a good way of scaring off predators. This copying of colours and patterns for protection is known as **Batesian mimicry**. Many stingless insects copy the form and colours of wasps, for example. They include the hornet clearwing moth (*Sepia apiformis*) and several species of hoverfly.

Not all creatures pretending to be something else copy the outfits of dangerous animals. Many just make themselves look more fearsome than they actually are. One of the most common ways of doing this is with **eyespots**. By flashing eye-like markings animals can scare predators off or startle them long enough to make an escape.

DECEPTIVE APPEARANCE Eyespots are used by harmless insects such as the western tiger swallowtail caterpillar (*Papilao rutulus*, left) and owl butterfly (*Caligo* species, below) to startle predators.

Disappearing into the background

Camouflage allows animals to hide from their predators or from their prey. A few species mimic not just the colour of their surroundings but the shape of objects within them. The giant frogfish (*Antennariidae commersonii*) for example, perfectly matches the corals it hides among to ambush prey.

HIDDEN HUNTER The Malaysian horned frog (*Megophrys nasuta*) lies in wait for prey.

④

How colours are made

⑥

◆ Most of the colours that we see in animals are formed by chemical compounds called **pigments**.
◆ Black, brown, dull reds and yellows are caused by the pigment **melanin**, which is made in animals' bodies. Some animals produce more melanin than others and are said to be melanistic (the black panther is a melanistic animal). Others produce no melanin at all and are albino.
◆ Bright oranges, reds and yellows are caused by **carotenoid** pigments. These are produced by plants, and animals obtain them through food. Carotenoids can be altered by animals to create other colours, such as blue.
◆ A few animals, such as cuttlefish and chameleons, can change their colour through **coloured skin cells** called chromatophores, which they can expand or contract individually.

RED TO GREEN This New Guinea green tree python (*Chondropython viridis*) is a juvenile. As it grows older it will gain the green colour that earns the species its name.

Tie-breaker

⑤

Q: **What is a tawny frogmouth?**
A: **A bird.** This Australian relative of the nightjar spends the day in the trees camouflaged as a broken branch. Its disguise is so good that it is hardly ever noticed, despite being relatively common.

⭐ 523

Putting on a show

Competition for mates takes many forms. For many **birds** colour and pattern play a central role. Species such as the peacock (*Pavo cristatus*) and the superb bird of paradise (*Lophorina superba*) grow dazzling feathers to **impress potential partners**. Almost without exception it is male birds with bright plumage. Females tend to be more dowdy to camouflage them on the nest.

Other creatures that use colour to attract mates include **lizards** and **fish**. Again, it is the males with the gaudy outfits; examples include the bright red and blue common agama lizard (*Agama agama*) from Africa and the orange fairy basslet (*Pseudanthias squamipinnis*), a denizen of tropical coral reefs.

TALL TAIL The peacock's tail feathers are grown and displayed to attract females. Perfect tail feathers indicate a fit individual and good potential mate.

Courtship and breeding

Creating a generation ❶

◆ The ability to reproduce is a defining characteristic of all lifeforms. Animals reproduce either **asexually** or **sexually**.

◆ In **asexual** reproduction a new animal buds off from the original. Many simple animals and some insects replicate themselves in this way.

◆ In **sexual** reproduction two individuals of different sexes mate to produce young. All vertebrate animals reproduce sexually.

◆ Animals find and **choose a mate** in a variety of ways. Some follow signals left by individuals of the opposite sex. Others gather at certain times to fight for the right to mate or to compete for potential partners.

Getting the message ❷

Animals that live **solitary lifestyles** give off signals when they are ready to breed. Some use **sound** – the female red fox (*Vulpes vulpes*) utters a high-pitched bark when she comes into season.

Others use odour to attract a mate. The **scent marks** of female territorial mammals tell wandering males whether or not a female is in season. And female moths waft out **pheromones** when they are ready to mate.

POWERUL ANTENNAE The male emperor moth (*Eudia pavonia*) can detect a female from 11 km (7 miles) away.

Fighting for mates ❸

The main alternative to using display to attract mates (see page 47) is fighting for them. **Most male mammals** fight for groups of females or the best breeding territories. Fighting for mates can be vicious but is almost never fatal. Most mammals have **ritualised displays** which enable rivals to size each other up and ensure that poorly matched males never fight. Male red deer (*Cervus elephus*), for example, indicate size and condition by roaring.

When most animals do fight it is to establish which one is **stronger** rather than to try to injure each other. To help them do this some mammals have **horns or antlers** which they lock together in head-to-head contests. Stag beetles have similar structures which they use in the same way.

Building a relationship ❹

Rather than fight or compete on physical appearance a few species create objects to entice a mate. Male **bowerbirds** build structures that seem to have no practical purpose at all, other than showing females how artistic they are. Different species of these Australasian birds build different-shaped bowers and each decorates theirs with objects of a particular colour. The satin bowerbird (*Ptilonorhynchus violaceus*, left) uses blue objects, for example.

Other birds build more practical structures to attract females. The male **weaverbird** from Africa builds a nest that a potential mate can actually lay her eggs in. Some fish play a similar mating game. The male **three-spined stickleback** (*Gasterosteus aculeatus*) builds an algae nest which must meet strict requirements before a female will consent to lay her eggs in it.

CLASH OF THE TITANS
A pair of male southern elephant seals (*Mirounga leonina*) do battle for a patch of beach.

One mate or many? ❺

◆ Some types of animal have more mates than others. Among mammals, the record for the **most mates in one breeding season** is held by the northern fur seal (*Callorhinus ursinus*). One male from the Pribilof Islands, Alaska, mated with 161 different females. A single northern elephant seal (*Mirounga angustirostris*) may keep a harem of 100 or more.

◆ **Monogamy is uncommon** in the animal kingdom. Where it does occur, it is most often among species where both parents are needed to bring up the young. **Most birds** are monogamous – at least for the duration of the breeding season. A few, such as the mute swan (*Cygnus olor*) and wandering albatross (*Diomedea exulans*), keep the same partner year after year (at up to 85 days the wandering albatross has the longest incubation period of any bird).

◆ A **small number** of **mammals** practise monogamy too. The most notable examples are Africa's oribi (*Ourebia ourebi*), klipspringer (*Oreotragus oreotragus*) and dik-diks (*Madoqua* species). These dwarf antelopes form couples that stay together in the same territory for the whole of their adult lives.

⭐ 249

Leks

Some male mammals and birds compete at **display grounds** for mates. These sites, known as leks, enable females to pick the most vigorous males to increase the chances that their young will be healthy.

No safety in numbers ❻

All breeding animals are either k- or r-strategists. **K-strategists** produce just a few offspring which they spend considerable time and effort looking after. **R-strategists** produce large numbers of young which they leave to fend for themselves. Most birds and mammals are k-strategists.

Tie-breaker ❼

Q: What type of animal is a beachmaster?
A: A male seal. Beachmasters control particular areas of breeding beaches and have mating rights over any females that choose that area to pup. Only the largest and fittest males become beachmasters and they have to fight to defend their position. In genetic terms the risks are worth taking; beachmasters can father dozens of pups, while males with no position on the beach rarely mate at all.

Growth and development

From birth to adulthood ❶

◆ Animals are **born or hatch** at different stages of development. Some, such as reptiles, emerge as miniature replicas of their parents. Others, such as birds, start life looking quite different from the adults that they will grow into.

◆ Baby animals that can **feed themselves** and walk from birth are said to be nidifugous.

Those that must be **looked after** by their parents are nidicolous.

◆ Some animals **reach full size** in a matter of months, while others take years to grow into adults. Most baby mammals, including humans, are born with their eyes full size – their heads and bodies grow around them.

Breaking out ❷

Many animals **shed their skin** at certain times in their lives. Arthropods such as arachnids and crustaceans must do this in order to grow. The 'skin' they are shedding is their tough outer skeleton (exoskeleton) and the process is called ecdysis. It often takes several hours for the new skeleton to harden.

Most vertebrates lose skin cells constantly as dust and replace them as they go. But snakes and lizards shed their entire skins at once, a process known as sloughing (pronounced sluffing).

Naming babies ❸

English has many words for young animals. The young of some species may be referred to by more than one of them.

Name	Used for young of:
Calf	Cattle, moose, whales, dolphins, rhinos, okapi, giraffe, hippos, camels, antelopes, elephants
Chick	All birds other than those which have specific terms for their offspring
Cria	Llama, alpaca, guanaco, vicuña
Cub	Bears, big cats, puma, cheetah, foxes, wolf, giant panda, badger
Cygnet	Swans
Duckling	Ducks
Eaglet	Eagles
Elver	Eels
Eyas	Hawks, falcons
Fawn	Deer, pronghorn
Foal	Horses
Fry	Fish
Gosling	Geese
Kid	Goats, gazelles
Kitten	Domestic cat, small wild cats, rabbits
Lamb	Sheep
Piglet	Pig
Poult	Turkey
Pullet	Chicken
Pup	Dogs, wolf, foxes, sea lions and seals, walrus

SHINY AND NEW A northern green gecko (*Naultinus grayii*) emerges from its old skin.

Parental responsibility ❹

Animals put different amounts of effort into bringing up their young. Many simply leave their offspring to fend for themselves. The animals that spend the most time and energy caring for their young are the mammals. Elephants suckle their calves for up to four years and many mammals continue to look after their offspring once they are weaned.

TOUGH LOVE The female white rhinoceros (*Ceratotherium simum*) protects her offspring until the calf is well over a year old.

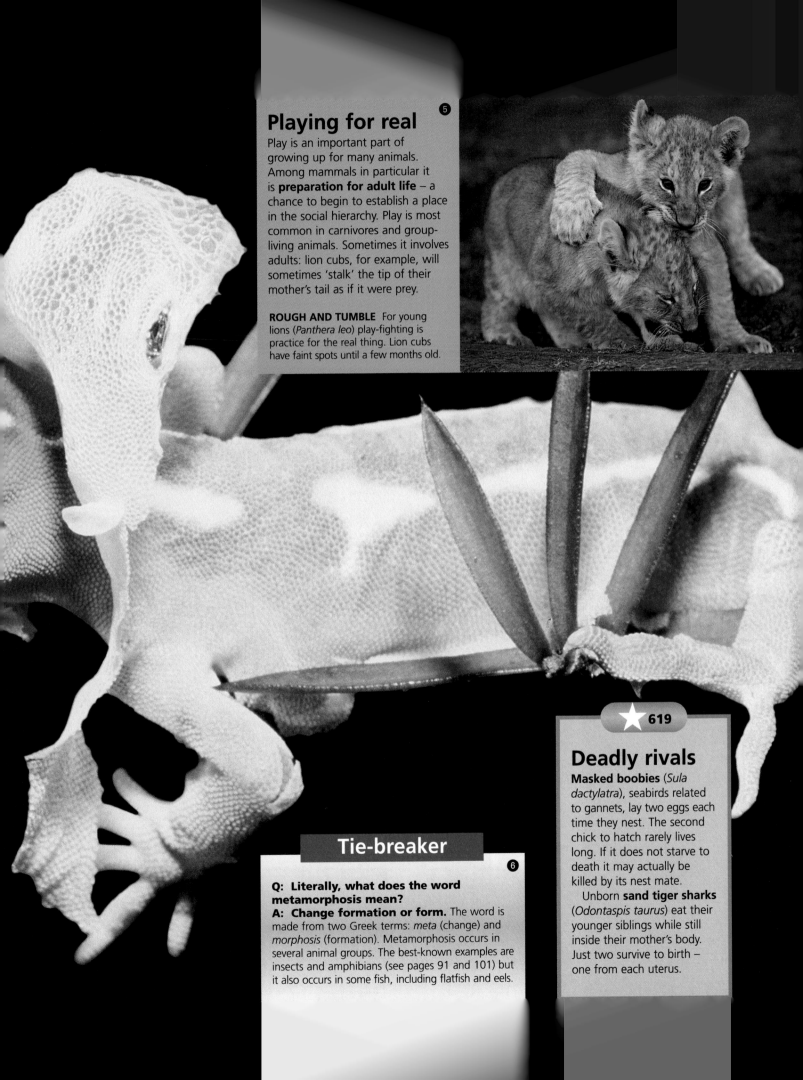

Playing for real ❺

Play is an important part of growing up for many animals. Among mammals in particular it is **preparation for adult life** – a chance to begin to establish a place in the social hierarchy. Play is most common in carnivores and group-living animals. Sometimes it involves adults: lion cubs, for example, will sometimes 'stalk' the tip of their mother's tail as if it were prey.

ROUGH AND TUMBLE For young lions (*Panthera leo*) play-fighting is practice for the real thing. Lion cubs have faint spots until a few months old.

Tie-breaker ❻

Q: Literally, what does the word metamorphosis mean?
A: Change formation or form. The word is made from two Greek terms: *meta* (change) and *morphosis* (formation). Metamorphosis occurs in several animal groups. The best-known examples are insects and amphibians (see pages 91 and 101) but it also occurs in some fish, including flatfish and eels.

⭐ **619**

Deadly rivals

Masked boobies (*Sula dactylatra*), seabirds related to gannets, lay two eggs each time they nest. The second chick to hatch rarely lives long. If it does not starve to death it may actually be killed by its nest mate.

Unborn **sand tiger sharks** (*Odontaspis taurus*) eat their younger siblings while still inside their mother's body. Just two survive to birth – one from each uterus.

Predators

Killing to live ❶

◆ Predators sit at the top of every food chain. Also known as **secondary consumers** (as opposed to primary consumers, which eat plants, and producers, the plants themselves), they hunt and kill other animals to survive.
◆ Predatory animals display an enormous **range of techniques** for catching prey. Some pursue quarry, alone or in groups; others sit and wait. Many creatures build traps to ensnare victims, while some use lures or kill with poison. A few meat-eaters bypass the hunting process altogether and scavenge for a living.
◆ Predators are always **less numerous** than plant-eaters. For this reason, and because they often threaten humans or livestock, they make up the majority of endangered species.

STONY STARE The stonefish (*Synanceia verrucosa*) stays stock still until prey passes by.

Surprise attack ❷

Many predators approach their prey stealthily, hidden by cover, or lie in wait for it to come into reach. This technique, known as **ambush** hunting, occurs throughout the animal kingdom. Well-known ambush predators include the tiger (*Panthera tigris*) and the praying mantis (*Mantis* spp).

Using traps ❹

A few predators make structures to capture prey. The most ingenious trap builders are the **spiders**. Many make webs to intercept insects and some disguise burrows from which they burst out to catch prey. One species makes a blanket which it covers with sand and hides under, while the ogre-faced spider (*Deinopis longipes*) casts a net of silk over its victims.

Trap-making insects include the European antlion (*Myrmeleon formicarius*). As a larva it digs a pit in sandy soil, then waits at the bottom for insects to slide in.

LYING IN WAIT
Trapdoor spiders (right) live in burrows with hinged lids. At night the lid is opened slightly so that the spider can listen for prey: when a victim comes into range the spider bursts out. All spiders have pedipalps on either side of their jaws. These appendages are extremely long in some trapdoor spider species.

Working together ❸

Hunting in groups enables predators to **tackle larger prey**. Prides of lions (*Panthera leo*) have been known to kill rhinos and young elephants – quarry that a single lion could not bring down alone. Coordinated hunting occurs mostly among mammals. One of the few bird species to do it is the white pelican (*Pelecanus onocrotalus*), which swims in formation to herd fish into shallow water.

AIR RAIDER A magnificent frigatebird (*Fregata magnificens*) forces a brown booby (*Sula leucogaster*) to give up its catch.

Stealing a meal ⑤

Many meat-eaters do not bother with hunting at all. Instead, they make a living by scavenging or stealing from others. **Skuas** and **frigatebirds**, for example, survive by bullying smaller seabirds into dropping or regurgitating their prey, which they then take for themselves.

Scavenging from the kills of others is something that most meat-eaters do but very few do exclusively. **Vultures** and **hyenas** specialise in scavenging. Spotted hyenas (*Crocuta crocuta*) have the **most powerful jaws** of any land carnivore, capable of crushing bones to get at the marrow inside. They are also hunters, killing about half of their food themselves.

Using venom ⑥

Many predators use poison to kill or immobilise prey. Among **reptiles** there are two venomous lizards and over 700 species of venomous snake (the **most venomous** of all is the sea snake *Hydrophis belcheri*). Poisonous snakes are either front-fanged and live on land, or back-fanged, which can be land or marine species. With the exception of Africa's boomslang, back-fanged snakes rarely kill people because the position of their fangs (at the rear of the mouth) makes it hard for them to inject sufficient venom.

READY TO STRIKE The hog-nosed viper (*Bothrops nasutus*) from Central America is a front-fanged snake.

FEMALE HUNTERS A group of lionesses bring down a zebra on the African plains.

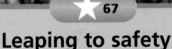

★ 67

Leaping to safety

Some hoofed mammals jump to get away from predators. A few, such as Africa's **springbok** (*Antidorcas marsupialis*), jump with all four feet at once: a technique known as pronking. Although just 90 cm (3 ft) tall they can leap up to 4 m (13 ft).

Tie-breaker ⑦

Q: How does the alligator snapping turtle lure its prey?
A: By wiggling its tongue. This huge North American turtle, which can exceed 1 m (3 ft 3 in) in length, lies on the bottom of lakes and rivers, wiggling its worm-like tongue to attract fish. This is unique among reptiles but not vertebrates as a whole. The anglerfish, for example, dangles its bait from a spiny rod protruding from between its eyes.

Defence and protection

Talking tactics ❶

◆ Many animals are too small or too slow to escape from predators and so have to come up with a wide range of **defence mechanisms**.
◆ Some of these mechanisms are physical, for instance being too **well-armoured** to kill or too **spiky** to swallow. Others are behavioural, such as **playing dead**.
◆ Some physical defence mechanisms have evolved more than once, resulting in animals that look similar but are actually unrelated.

Armour plated ❷

Many animals have a built-in suit of armour. **Armadillos** are protected by horny plates joined together by flexible skin, while **pangolins** are covered with scales of modified hair. The shells of **turtles** and **tortoises** are made from bone and are actually part of the creature's skeleton. **Armoured fish** include **seahorses** and **dragonfish**, and **shelled invertebrates** are extremely common: virtually all **molluscs** are protected by **shells** and most **crustaceans** have a tough outer skeleton.

TOTAL COVER The nine-banded armadillo (*Dasypus novemcinctus*) can roll up into an impenetrable ball.

A prickly mouthful ❸

Spikes or spines make for a very unpleasant meal and several types of animal have evolved them. **Among mammals,** hedgehogs, tenrecs, echidnas and **porcupines** all have spines. Those of porcupines, known as quills, come away and have barbs that cause them to work their way into an attacker's flesh. An entire class of invertebrates, the **sea urchins**, are protected by spines, and have changed little in 500 million years.

HARD TO SWALLOW Porcupine fish (*Diodon* species) are not only spiky but can inflate themselves into a ball.

★ 768

Creating a smoke screen

Cuttlefish confuse predators with a cloud of ink. These intelligent molluscs fire the pigment into the water as they make their escape. Cuttlefish ink was the original substance used to create the artists' ink sepia. In recognition of this all cuttlefish have the word sepia, or derivations of it, in their Latin names.

STINGS LIKE A BEE The boxer crab (above) carries stinging sea anemones on its pincers and uses them to 'punch' potential predators.

Unusual strategies ❹

Most methods of deterring predators occur in many species throughout the animal kingdom. But a few are unique to just one or a small number of animals.

◆ **Skunks** are the only vertebrates to **spray their enemies** with smelly fluid. The noxious substance, produced by glands beneath the tail, makes other animals choke and retch and can be smelled from more than a kilometre away.

◆ Some insects behave in a similar manner but with different ammunition. **Wood ants** (*Formica rufa*) fire formic acid while the **bombardier beetle** (*Brachinus crepitans*) shoots a vapour that explodes as it mixes with air.

◆ An even stranger behaviour that seems to work is **playing dead**. Europe's **grass snake** (*Natrix natrix*) does this, as does the **Virginia opossum** (*Didelphis virginiana*).

Leaving a bad taste ❺

One of the best ways to avoid being eaten is to **be inedible**. All sorts of animals are either poisonous or taste so foul that predators leave them alone. **Shrews** exude a foul-smelling fluid from glands in their skin. Many **amphibians** also avoid predation by secreting noxious or toxic substances.

Scare tactics ❻

◆ **Looking dangerous** is a good way to get out of trouble. Some creatures, particularly insects (see page 46), achieve this by mimicking larger animals.

◆ A few creatures **puff themselves up** to look bigger. The **common toad** (*Bufo bufo*) does just that when confronted by a predator, for instance, standing on tiptoes at the same time to appear taller as well.

◆ **Cats** and **dogs** have hairs on their shoulders called hackles which they raise when threatened. Even **elephants** spread out their ears to appear bigger than they actually are.

◆ Another display, common among carnivores and primates, is **baring teeth**. Most mammals also make a lot of **noise** when attacked in an attempt to frighten their enemy.

RUFF BLUFF Australia's harmless frilled lizard (*Chlamydosaurus kingii*) erects its neck frill and hisses when attacked.

Parasites and symbiosis

Made for each other ①

◆ No animal is truly independent: all interact with other species to some degree. But some relationships are closer than others. **Parasitic** and **symbiotic** associations are the closest of all.
◆ **Parasites** are **unable to survive** without a host creature, and often, though not always, harm the host in the process. In a **symbiotic** association, **both species benefit**, and in extreme cases, neither could survive alone.
◆ **Symbiosis** has a huge influence on the natural world. Without symbiosis there would be no hummingbirds, flowers or butterflies. Nor would there be any coral reefs – algae live symbiotically inside most corals (see page 87).

Unlikely ② allies

◆ **Symbiotic relationships** between animals often revolve around food. Africa's **honey badger** (*Mellivora capensis*) and **honeyguide** (*Indicator indicator*) both enjoy honey: the honeyguide, a bird, has a talent for finding it and the honey badger is specialised for breaking into beehives.
◆ Some fish live by feeding on the parasites of others. **Cleaner wrasses** attract larger fish to special cleaning stations where they rid them of fish lice and other unwanted guests. **Cleaner shrimps** perform a similar service.
◆ A third kind of symbiosis exists between some tropical marine **gobies** and **blind shrimps**. While the fish keeps watch the shrimp maintains a burrow, which both creatures use to hide from predators.

OPEN WIDE Cleaner shrimps remove parasites from a tomato cod (*Lysmatia amboinesis*).

★ 98

Animals that live on us

A wide range of animals parasitise humans. **Parasitic insects** include lice (*Pediculus* species), the human flea (*Pulex irritans*) and bedbugs (*Cimex* species). **Arachnid parasites** include various ticks and mites, such as the scabies mite (*Sarcoptes scabiei*).

Most **endoparasites** fall under the broad heading of worms (see page 86). Among the most dangerous to people are the pork tapeworm (*Taenia solium*), the blood flukes (*Schistosoma* species), and a nematode worm called *Wuchereria bancrofti*.

ITCHY SCALP The human head louse, or nit (*Pediculus humanus*), occurs worldwide. It feeds on blood and can transmit typhus.

③ Milking aphids

Many **aphids** escape predators by associating with **ants**. In return for the ants' protection the tiny insects produce a sugary substance called honeydew, which the ants feed on.

Tie-breaker

4

Q: What behaviour links Europe's cuckoo and North America's cowbird?
A: They both lay their eggs in other birds' nests.
The cuckoo (*Cuculus canorus*) parasitises the nests of warblers and a few other small birds. Cowbirds (*Molothrus ater*) are less choosy – their chicks may be raised by any one of more than 220 different host species.

A glossary of terms

5

Parasite	An organism that draws shelter and food from another while contributing nothing to its host's survival.
Host	An organism on or in which a parasite lives.
Ectoparasite	A parasite that lives on the outer surface of its host.
Endoparasite	A parasite that lives inside its host.
Symbiosis	A relationship between individuals of different species that benefits both parties (also called mutualism).
Symbiont	One party in a symbiotic relationship.

The birds and bees

6

Most **flowers** are a product of symbiosis. They produce nectar to attract insects and other flying creatures such as hummingbirds which then spread the plant's pollen. Both sides gain from this relationship; the nectar feeds the animal and the animal provides a courier service for the plant, ensuring that none of its pollen is wasted.

This symbiotic relationship led to the evolution of whole orders of animals. The **first flowers** appeared around 150 million years ago, and were quickly followed by the first butterflies, nectar-feeding moths and bees.

Life among anemones

7

Few animals survive long among a sea anemones' stinging tentacles, but one group of Indo-Pacific fishes actually makes them its home. **Anemonefish** exude slimy mucus containing chemicals which prevent the anemone's cells from firing. Anemonefish are poor swimmers and find safety from predators among the tentacles. The benefits to the anemone are less clear.

TROPICAL COLOUR The clown anemonefish (*Amphiprion percula*) occurs from Queensland to Vanuatu.

QUESTION NUMBER The numbers or star following the answers refer to information boxes on the right.

ANSWERS

35	Alpha **8**
★ 61	D: It dies ★
92	Workers **3**
155	Troop – another term for monkeys is tribe
233	A wolf **8**
333	Flock **5**
371	A pride **2**
461	Herd **5**
462	Pack **8**
463	Raft **2**
464	Hover **2**
465	Smack **2**
466	Murmuration **2**
467	Shrewdness **2**
468	Murder **2**
469	Crash **2**
470	Mob **2**
509	Bees **3**
524	Female **3**
558	Ants **3**
842	Prairie dog **7**
967	Lupus **8**

Groups and societies

Why live together? **1**

◆ Many animals spend their lives surrounded by others of their kind. The groups that they form evolve for different reasons and have varying levels of complexity.

◆ The **simplest** aggregations are those formed for **defence**. Individuals have little interaction with other members of the group, except as lookouts or shields for their own protection.

◆ Groups formed by **carnivores** have structures based on a **dominance hierarchy**. This decides who gets to feed first at a kill and also sometimes who gets to breed.

◆ The **most complex** animal societies are those of **insects**. In these the majority of members never breed but spend their lives working for and defending the colony as a whole.

Family gatherings **2**

Did you know that a group of finches is called a charm? Below are 40 more terms used to describe groups of birds and animals.

Creature	Group	Creature	Group
Apes	Shrewdness	Jellyfish	Smack
Badgers	Cete	Kangaroos	Mob
Bats	Colony	Lions	Pride
Butterflies	Flight	Magpies	Tiding
Capercaillies	Tok	Owls	Parliament
Caterpillars	Army	Parrots	Company
Crows	Murder	Partridges	Covey
Doves	Piteousness	Peacocks	Ostentation
Ducks	Raft, team	Quails	Bevy, drift
Eagles	Convocation	Ravens	Unkindness
Eels	Swarm	Rhinoceroses	Crash
Ferrets	Business	Salmon	Bind
Frogs	Army	Sheep	Flock
Geese	Gaggle, skein	Snipe	Wisp
Gorillas	Whoop	Starlings	Murmuration
Grouse	Covey	Storks	Mustering
Guillemots	Loomery	Trout	Hover
Hares	Trip	Turkeys	Rafter
Hedgehogs	Array	Whales	Pod, school
Herons	Siege	Wild boars	Sounder

SEA OF BODIES Hundreds of snappers (*Salema* species) school off the Galapagos islands.

WEIRD AND WONDERFUL 4 A species of **ant** (*Linepithema humile*) introduced to Europe from Argentina has formed the **largest supercolony** ever recorded. The colony contains billions of individuals and stretches from Italy to the far northwest of Spain.

Insect societies **3**

Four types of insect live in complex societies: ants, termites, wasps and bees. All form nests based around a breeding female, the queen, whose single object in life is to produce offspring. The queen is often many times larger than the other colony members.

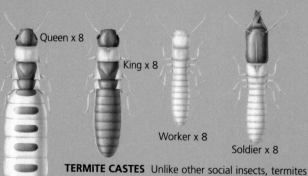

Queen x 8

King x 8

Worker x 8

Soldier x 8

TERMITE CASTES Unlike other social insects, termites have a single breeding male, the king. These are *Kalotermes flavicollis*, a European wood-boring species.

Lost in the crowd ❺

◆ Many animals live in groups **for protection**. By gathering together they make it harder for predators to catch them; more eyes mean that danger is more easily spotted and individuals in groups are harder to target than they are on their own.

◆ The **largest** such gatherings known are those of **krill**. One swarm, tracked off Antarctica in 1981, was estimated to contain more than 500 billion animals.

◆ Except where they have specific words to describe them (see *Family gatherings*) **groups of mammals** are known as herds, groups of **birds** as flocks and groups of **fish** as schools or shoals.

Tie-breaker ❻

Q: What is a group of spotted hyenas called?
A: A clan. Spotted, or laughing, hyenas (*Crocuta crocuta*) live in clans of **up to 80** individuals – the largest social groups of any carnivore. Clans are dominated by females, which are larger and more aggressive than the males. Several females in a clan may have young at any one time. Uniquely among social carnivores, there is no cooperation in bringing up the young.

⭐ **61**

Dying for queen and colony

Honeybees die when they sting an intruder. They give up their lives because they share 75 per cent of their genes with the queen. Worker bees cannot reproduce, and even if they could would only pass on half of their genes through mating. By dying for the queen they are protecting their own gene line.

City dwellers

◆ Before the arrival of Europeans, **prairie dogs** (*Cynomys* species) lived across much of North America. Today, these sociable rodents are restricted mostly to reserves, the prairies having made way for farmland.

◆ Prairie dogs live in groups called **coteries**, which inhabit a network of burrows. Breeding coteries contain an adult male and about four females with their young. Non-breeding coteries may have several males and females.

◆ Each coterie defends a territory above ground which borders the territories of others. These territories form **'towns'** which may cover a wide area.

Pack life ❽

Group living enables predators to hunt larger prey and to hold larger territories than they could on their own.

Among carnivores, group living is most common in dogs. **Wolves** (*Canis lupus*) and **Cape hunting dogs** (*Lycaon pictus*) live in packs, led by a single breeding pair; the **alpha** male and female. With the support of other pack members these individuals can raise many more offspring.

OVERWHELMING FORCE A pack of Cape hunting dogs can overpower almost any prey.

Animal engineers

The need to create **1**

◆ Most creatures sleep and give birth out in the open but some create **shelters** for themselves and their young. A few use, and sometimes modify, objects from their surroundings as **tools**, usually to obtain food.
◆ Perhaps the most familiar structures built by animals are **birds' nests**, but many **insects**, such as bees and paper wasps, also build nests. Other invertebrate engineers include termites and web-spinning spiders (see page 93).
◆ **Mammals** are better known for **burrowing** than building. The tunnels they excavate range from simple chambers with a single entrance to sprawling networks shared by many individuals.

Tool users **2**

Tool use is usually associated with apes, but many other creatures use tools in nature. The **Egyptian vulture** (*Neophron percnopterus*) throws stones to break ostrich eggs, for instance, while the **sea otter** (*Enhydra lutra*) uses a pebble balanced on its chest to crack open shellfish. In Japan **carrion crows** (*Corvus corone*) even make use of human tools. They place walnuts in front of cars that are stopped at red traffic lights. When the lights change the cars move, cracking the nuts.

CHIMP CUTLERY Some chimps (*Pan troglodytes*) push twigs into ants' nests to collect the insects for food.

Somewhere to call home **3**

Many burrows and hideaways have their own particular names.

Animal	Home	Description
Bear *Family Ursidae*	Den	Cave used for hibernation and giving birth
Beaver *Castor fiber*	Lodge	Wooden structure surrounded by water, with an underwater entrance
Black-tailed prairie dog *Cynomys ludovicianus*	Town	Numerous separate burrows dug close together
Brown hare *Lepus europaeus*	Form	Depression amid long grass for hiding leverets (young)
Common rabbit *Oryctolagus cuniculus*	Warren	Tunnel network that may be home to up to 30 individuals
Eurasian badger *Meles meles*	Sett	Huge tunnel networks with numerous entrances
Eurasian otter *Lutra lutra*	Holt (den)	Burrow; territory also has lying-up places known as hovers
Grey wolf *Canis lupus*	Den	Natural cave used for giving birth
Honeybee *Apis mellifera*	Hive	Structure of multiple hexagonal chambers made from beeswax
Red fox *Vulpes vulpes*	Earth or den	Burrow used for giving birth

Avian architects

Almost all birds build nests to **contain their eggs**. These vary from simple scrapes in the ground to elaborate hanging baskets and houses of mud. A few species build **communal nests**. Africa's social weavers (*Philetairus socius*), for instance, live in nests that may contain 300 pairs. The **largest nests** are those built by eagles, which add new material to them year after year. The biggest ever recorded was built by bald eagles (*Haliaeetus leucocephalus*) and measured 2.8 m (9 ft 6 in) wide and 6 m (20 ft) deep.

NOISY NEIGHBOURS North American cliff swallows (*Petrochelidon pyrrhonota*) nest together.

★ **283**

Saliva stew

Bird's nest soup has been eaten in China for more than 1500 years. The nests used are those of the edible-nest swiftlet (*Aerodramus fuciphagus*), which builds them from sticky saliva secreted from a pair of extra large glands.

TENT MAKERS Honduran white bats (*Lectophylla alba*) use leaves to create rain-proof roosts.

Burrowers and builders

Most **mammals that burrow** do so to hide from predators and the elements, but some live underground. **Moles** and **mole-rats** rarely see the sun. The former spend their time hunting for earthworms while the latter eat tubers and roots.

Only a **few mammals build** structures, the best known example being the **beaver**, which alters its environment more than any animal apart from man, felling trees to dam rivers and create the artificial lakes where it lives. The longest beaver dam ever measured, in Montana, USA, was 700 m (2300 ft) long.

HANGING ON The male black-headed weaver (*Ploceus cucullatus*) builds his intricate nest to attract a mate.

Evolution and extinction

What is evolution? ❶

◆ Evolution is **change over generations** in response to physical conditions – animals evolve to cope with changes in their environment. In the process they become altered, sometimes into completely new forms.
◆ The process of evolution was first noticed and explained by the scientist **Charles Darwin**.

What he said was controversial in a world then believed to have been created by God in seven days. Backed up with compelling evidence, Darwin's theory explained much that had previously been unexplained about the natural world, such as why similar looking but unrelated animals appeared around the globe.

Darwin's life ❷

Charles Darwin (1809–82) was born in Shrewsbury, England. After obtaining a degree in theology from Christ's College, Cambridge, in 1831 he joined a five-year surveying expedition to Patagonia on the HMS *Beagle*. During this he visited the Galapagos islands. Darwin's *Origin of Species by Means of Natural Selection* was published in 1859.

FIRST BIRD The earliest known bird is *Archaeopteryx*, discovered in Germany in 1861. The rocks that yielded its fossils have been dated at just over **146 million years** old.

★ 219

Life's hidden history

More than two million animal species have been discovered and named, and there may be as many as 100 million in total. But all of them are just a fraction of the creatures that have existed. Although we know about some extinct animals from **fossils**, most will remain unknown forever.

Fossils form only in certain environments, so the chances of an animal becoming a fossil are slim. The chances of any fossils that do form surviving and then being discovered are even slimmer. Scientists estimate that as much as 99 per cent of all life that existed has now disappeared forever without leaving a trace.

FIRST MAMMAL The earliest mammals were small, shrew-like creatures, such as *Morganucodon*. They evolved at around the same time as the dinosaurs, **230 million years** ago.

EXTINCTION EVENT At the end of the Palaeozoic Era **245 million years** ago 95 per cent of all life on Earth was wiped out.

If only she could talk ❸

The oldest resident of the Australian Zoo in Queensland saw Charles Darwin with her own eyes. Harriet, a giant tortoise, was taken from the Galapagos islands to England in 1835 aboard the *Beagle*. In 1841 she was shipped to Australia and housed at Brisbane's Botanical gardens. Harriet is the world's **oldest known living vertebrate**. In 2002 she celebrated her 172nd birthday.

SLOW BUT SURE Harriet the Galapagos giant tortoise (*Geochelone elephantopus*) is the oldest known land animal.

EXTINCTION EVENT The dinosaurs and numerous other animal groups disappeared **65 million years** ago. The event marked the end of the Mesozoic Era.

FIRST ANIMALS The earliest animals are believed to have appeared around **720 million years** ago. The oldest fossils of animals, such as *Dickinsonia*, date back around 600 million years.

Human evolution ❹

The most controversial of Darwin's ideas was that humans evolved from more primitive apes. Some people still debate that claim but there is now overwhelming fossil and genetic evidence to back it up. The first ape, *Proconsul*, appeared 25 million years ago. From it a line can be drawn to *Homo habilis* and through *Homo erectus* and *Homo heidelbergensis* to ourselves, *Homo sapiens sapiens*. Neanderthals (*Homo neanderthalensis*) were not our ancestors but a closely related species.

HUMANS APPEAR *Homo habilis*, the first representative of our own genus, evolved **1.8 million years** ago. Our species, *Homo sapiens*, evolved 200 000–140 000 years ago. Modern man, *Homo sapiens sapiens*, appeared 120 000 years ago.

FIRST LIFE The oldest fossils are of stromatolites and are **3500 million years** old. Stromatolites are structures formed by communities of cyanobacteria, also known as blue-green algae.

❻

Inspirational islands ❺

Much of the evidence that Darwin cited for his theory of Natural Selection came from what he saw on the **Galapagos** islands. Darwin noticed, for instance, that the finches on each island were subtly different. While at first sight they all appeared to be members of the same species a closer look revealed differences in the shapes of their beaks.

Darwin linked these variations to differences in the birds' diets and was able to show that this was influenced by the availability of certain foods. As the finches had moved from island to island they had adapted to enable them to take advantage of the most abundant food sources, or even turn to new sources entirely.

FIRST FISH Early fish, such as *Arandaspis*, for which fossils exist, appear in rocks that formed **470 million years** ago.

FIRST REPTILE The oldest known reptile is the lizard-like *Hylonomus*. A hunter of insects and other invertebrates, it lived **310 million years** ago and grew to about 20 cm (8 in) long.

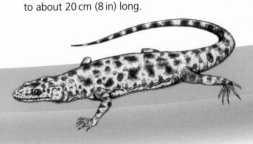

FIRST AMPHIBIANS Amphibians such as *Proterogyrinus* appeared **335 million years** ago. They were the first vertebrates to spend part of their lives on land.

Dinosaurs

Core facts ❶

◆ A dinosaur is any member of the **extinct vertebrate class** Dinosauria. Dinosaurs existed for around 165 million years and disappeared 65 million years ago.
◆ Dinosaurs were **land-living** animals; they could not fly and did not live in water.
◆ They had an **upright stance**; their legs were tucked beneath them like those of modern-day mammals.
◆ Most had **scaly skin** like today's reptiles, the exceptions being the few meat-eaters on the branch of the evolutionary tree that led to birds.
◆ Some dinosaurs ate plants and others ate meat. Almost all of them **laid eggs**.

Discovering dinosaurs ❷

The first person to publish a description of a dinosaur was an Englishman named William Buckland in 1824. His discovery, *Megalosaurus*, was followed a year later by Gideon Mantell's description of the first plant-eating dinosaur, *Iguanodon*. Since then more than **1650** different dinosaurs **have been discovered** and named – we now have examples from every continent, including Antarctica. The search for new dinosaurs continues and has yielded impressive results. In 2001, 37 new species were described.

Dinosaur eggs ❸

Considering the size of dinosaurs themselves, the eggs they laid were quite small. The **largest egg** found (pictured) was laid by the **sauropod** *Hypselosaurus priscus*, and was 30 cm (12 in) long by 25.5 cm (10 in) wide.

Tracks and traces ❹

The reason that we know dinosaurs existed is because of the **fossils** they left behind. The most familiar fossils are bones but dinosaurs also left other traces of their passing. Fossilised tracks tell us how fast dinosaurs moved. And coprolites (fossilised dung) tell us what they ate. The largest known coprolite came from a *Tyrannosaurus rex* and is 44 cm (17½ in) long.

What's in a name? ❺

Name	Meaning
Allosaurus	Strange reptile
Ankylosaurus	Fused reptile
Brachiosaurus	Arm reptile
Diplodocus	Double beam
Iguanodon	Iguana tooth
Seismosaurus	Earthquake reptile
Stegosaurus	Roof reptile
Triceratops	Three-horned face
Tyrannosaurus rex	Tyrant lizard king
Velociraptor	Speedy predator

Dinosaur groups ❻

Dinosaur classification is an area of great debate among scientists. However, most experts agree that there were twelve major groups.

THEROPODS
All meat-eating dinosaurs belonged to this group. Therapods include the ancestors of modern birds.

SAUROPODS
The largest dinosaurs were all sauropods. Sauropods had long necks, small heads and simple, peglike teeth.

PROSAUROPODS
These looked like small sauropods. They had died out by the early Jurassic, before most sauropods existed.

STEGOSAURS
These plant-eaters had rows of large bony plates running down their backs. Most lived in the Jurassic.

ANKYLOSAURS
Also known as armoured dinosaurs, these plant-eaters had plates of bone embedded in their skin.

Food and feeding ❽

Dinosaurs included plant-eaters and meat-eaters. Most **plant-eating dinosaurs** swallowed their food whole and broke it down in their intestines; some had pebbles (gastroliths) in their gut to help them to do this. A few Cretaceous plant-eaters, such as *Iguanodon*, evolved the ability to chew, making their digestion more efficient.

Meat-eating dinosaurs swallowed their food whole. The largest could wolf down chunks of 70 kg (154 lb). Most meat-eating dinosaurs were armed with fearsome teeth and claws to kill their prey. The biggest toe claws belonged to *Megaraptor*, a gigantic relative of the better-known *Utahraptor* and *Velociraptor*.

DEADLY WEAPON *Tyrannosaurus rex* had the longest teeth of any dinosaur, each up to 15 cm (6 in) long. Thick but with serrated edges, they could rip through skin and pulverise bone.

A new king ❼

For 90 years *Tyrannosaurus rex* was the **biggest meat-eating land animal** the world had ever known. Then, in 1995, fossil hunters in South America found a predator that outstretched *Tyrannosaurus* by a full metre. They called their discovery *Giganotosaurus* (giant reptile). A close relative of *Allosaurus*, it lived 90 million years ago – more than 20 million years before *Tyrannosaurus* appeared.

★ 782

Jurassic lawn?

Plant-eating dinosaurs are often called grass-eaters but the fact is they never ate a single blade of the stuff. Grass did not appear until the Cenozoic Era – when the last dinosaurs had already died out.

When did the dinosaurs live? ❾

The time that the dinosaurs were on Earth is divided into three Periods.

◆ The first dinosaurs appeared in the first half of the **Triassic Period**, which began 245 million years ago and ended 208 million years ago.

◆ The Triassic was followed by the **Jurassic Period**, which lasted from 208 to 144 million years ago. This

saw the evolution of the first truly giant dinosaurs.

◆ The longest of the three Periods, the Cretaceous, lasted from 144 to 65 million years ago.

◆ The Triassic, Jurassic and Cretaceous Periods make up the **Mesozoic** ('middle life') Era, which sits between the Palaeozoic ('ancient life') and Cenozoic ('recent life') Eras.

Formation of the Earth | First life | **Mesozoic era** (Triassic, Jurassic, Cretaceous) | Present day

PACHYCEPHALOSAURS These two-legged plant-eaters are sometimes called bone-headed dinosaurs. Scientists believe that the males butted each other.

CERATOPIANS Also known as horned dinosaurs, this group of plant-eaters included *Triceratops*.

IGUANODONTIDS All members of this group had defensive 'thumb spikes'. They walked on all four feet but ran on their back legs.

HADROSAURS Commonly known as duck-billed dinosaurs, these plant-eaters evolved during the Cretaceous Period.

HYPSILOPHODONTIDS Few of these plant-eaters were bigger than a man and some were smaller than an Alsatian dog. They were mostly fast movers.

HETERODONTOSAURS This group of early plant-eaters contains just a few species. All were small and none survived beyond the early Jurassic Period.

FABROSAURS These include some of the smallest of all dinosaurs – some no bigger than a chicken.

Pterosaurs and sea reptiles

Core facts ❶

◆ **Pterosaurs** were closely related to dinosaurs: it is thought that the two shared a common ancestor in the early Triassic Period. They belong to the extinct class Pterosauria.
◆ Pterosaurs were the **first vertebrates to fly**. For the last 85 million years of their existence pterosaurs shared the skies with birds.
◆ Like birds, pterosaurs had **lightweight bones** filled with a honeycomb of air pockets.

◆ Pterosaurs flew on **wings of skin** stretched between their bodies and the end of an elongated fourth finger.
◆ While dinosaurs and pterosaurs existed the seas were filled by **giant marine reptiles**. There were five classes: Plesiosauria, Ichthyosauria, Nothosauria, Placodonta and Mosasauria.
◆ Pterosaurs and giant sea reptiles disappeared with the dinosaurs 65 million years ago.

Early discoveries ❷

Pterosaurs and giant sea reptiles were recognised several years before dinosaurs. The French anatomist Georges Cuvier named the first pterosaur *Pterodactylus* (meaning 'wing finger') in 1809. Just 12 years later the first giant sea reptile was discovered in England (see *Weird and Wonderful*) and named *Ichthyosaurus* by Henry de la Beche and William Conybeare.

The first dinosaur was not named until 1824 (see page 64). The word dinosaur was created by the English anatomist Richard Owen in 1841 from the Greek deinos, meaning 'terrible', and the Latin sauros, meaning 'lizards' or 'reptiles'.

Tie-breaker ❸

Q: Which modern marine reptiles lived alongside the dinosaurs?
A: Turtles. Turtles have existed since the Triassic. There are just five sea-going species today but there were once many more. The biggest, *Archelon*, was 4.5 m (15 ft) long. It died out 65 million years ago.

Ruling the waves ❹

◆ While dinosaurs walked the land and pterosaurs ruled the skies, the seas were dominated by gigantic marine reptiles. The two **most successful groups** were the ichthyosaurs and the plesiosaurs.
◆ Ichthyosaurs (meaning 'fish lizards') appeared before the first dinosaurs 240 million years ago. They included the fastest-swimming of all marine reptiles and by the early Jurassic had evolved a similar body form to modern dolphins.
◆ Plesiosaurs (meaning 'near lizards') appeared just after dinosaurs and evolved into two distinct forms: long-necked, fish-eating creatures such as *Cryptoclidus* and *Elasmosaurus*, and short-necked meat-eaters such as *Kronosaurus* and *Liopleurodon*. The short-necked plesiosaurs, or pliosaurs, became enormous. *Liopleurodon* is thought to have grown to 25 m (82 ft) long and weighed as much as 150 tonnes, making it the largest predator ever.

LONG-NECKED PLESIOSAUR
Elasmosaurus' neck contained a total of 76 vertebrae (bones) and was the longest of any sea reptile.

ICHTHYOSAUR
Ophthalmosaurus was one of the fastest animals in the ocean. Its large eyes suggest that it hunted at depth.

PLIOSAUR *Liopleurodon* hunted other sea reptiles during the Jurassic Period.

INSECT EATER
Peteinosaurus was one of the earliest pterosaurs.

Different types of pterosaur ⑤

◆ The **first pterosaurs** were small – few grew much bigger than a modern-day crow. They had long tails and their jaws were full of small teeth.

◆ Towards the end of the Jurassic Period new, larger pterosaurs began to appear. They had **no tails** and **fewer teeth**: by the beginning of the Cretaceous Period none had teeth at all. This made them **lighter** than they would otherwise have been and enabled some to grow **larger** than any flying creatures before or since.

◆ Pterosaurs had much more **delicate skeletons** than either dinosaurs or giant sea reptiles. As such they were less likely to form fossils and fewer than 120 species have been discovered so far.

WEIRD AND WONDERFUL ⑥

The first two giant sea reptiles to be described were discovered by Mary Anning. *Ichthyosaurus* (named in 1821) and *Plesiosaurus* (named in 1824) were both found in rocks near Lyme Regis, where she lived.

TEXAN TITAN Despite its size, *Quetzalcoatlus* was surprisingly light. Hollow bones meant that it weighed about 100 kg (220 lb), little more than a man.

★ **176**

The biggest flying animal ever

In 1971 a palaeontologist named Douglas Lawson made a discovery in Texas, USA, that was to stun the world. He unearthed a bone of immense proportions and announced that it had belonged to a pterosaur – an animal that could fly. The pterosaur was named **Quetzalcoatlus** after the feathered serpent god of the Aztecs. Subsequent finds confirmed that *Quetzalcoatlus* was the largest flying animal ever discovered, with a wingspan of at least 11 m (37 ft) – more than a Second World War Spitfire fighter plane.

The numbers or star following the answers refer to information boxes on the right.

ANSWERS

★	40	A sabretoothed cat ★
	109	Trilobites ❷
	218	False ❹
	789	True ★
	821	C: A sail ❶
	824	C: Squid ❷
	826	D: A bird ❺
	829	B: A shark ❼
	932	They swam in open water ❷
	935	Birds ❺
	936	Whales evolved after dinosaurs disappeared ❹
	986	False (it was a whale) ❹
	990	True ❻

Other prehistoric animals

Core facts ❶

◆ There has been **life on Earth** for most of its 4.6 billion-year history and animals for at least half a billion years. In that time a vast array of species have come and gone.
◆ The **earliest animals** were all invertebrates. Most were bizarre forms that we would not recognise, but some, such as jellyfish, still exist.
◆ The **first vertebrates** – fish – were followed by amphibians and reptiles. Before the age of the dinosaurs the land was ruled by more primitive giant reptiles such as *Dimetrodon*.
◆ The dinosaurs' extinction left a vacuum which was filled by birds and mammals. Some creatures which had evolved when the dinosaurs were alive, such as crocodiles, survived to live alongside the new dominant groups.

The first animals ❷

The first living things appeared more than three billion years before the first dinosaurs. For most of that time the planet was populated only by **single-celled organisms** such as bacteria, but 550 million years ago, as the Palaeozoic Era began, they were joined by a dazzling range of **marine invertebrates**.

One of the most successful groups was the **trilobites**, bottom-dwellers that looked a bit like woodlice but grew to 70 cm (2 ft) long. They evolved into thousands of different forms but had all died out by the beginning of the Mesozoic Era. Another successful group, the **ammonites**, survived long into the Mesozoic. Their close relatives, cephalopods such as the chambered nautilus (*Nautilus pompilius*) and squid, are still alive today. The first land animals were also invertebrates – molluscs and ancestors of modern arthropods (see page 92).

STONE SPIRAL
Ammonites are among the most familiar fossils. They existed for over 300 million years before dying out at the end of the Mesozoic Era.

Tie-breaker

❸

Q: *Deinosuchus* preyed on dinosaurs, but what type of animal was it?
A: A crocodile. *Deinosuchus* was the biggest crocodile that ever lived. At up to 15 m (50 ft) long and weighing 2 tonnes it could have given *Tyrannosaurus rex* a run for its money. *Deinosuchus* appeared in the arcade game of the film *Jurassic Park: The Lost World*, although it actually lived during the Cretaceous Period in North America.

 ★ 40

Sabretooth!

Sabretoothed cats were among the most fearsome predators ever. The first, small species appeared around five million years ago. Within three million years they had become giants. *Smilodon*, which existed in the Americas until just 11 000 years ago, was significantly larger than a modern tiger. Its canine teeth, designed for stabbing flesh and suffocating prey, were more than 18 cm (7 in) long.

The age of mammals ❹

After the dinosaurs died out the mammals took over. Mammals had already existed for 170 million years but now they evolved into **radically new forms** to fill the niches left empty by the dinosaurs' extinction. To replace the giant plant-eating dinosaurs huge mammals such as brontotheres, chalicotheres and elephants appeared. Meat-eaters included creodonts such as *Hyaenodon*, which grew to the size of a small rhinoceros. Even bigger was *Andrewsarchus*, at 5 m (16½ ft) long the largest meat-eating land mammal ever. The giant sea reptiles were replaced by whales such as *Basilosaurus*.

Early birds ❺

The **first birds** appeared about 150 million years ago during the Jurassic Period and most scientists agree that they evolved from meat-eating dinosaurs. Fossils from China of what appear to be **feathered dinosaurs** back this up. Four such dinosaurs are known: *Sinosauropteryx* found in 1996; *Protarchaeopteryx* found in 1997; and *Caudipteryx* and *Confuciusornis* found in 1998. The **earliest known true bird** is *Archaeopteryx*, discovered in Germany in 1861. After the dinosaurs died out many new types of bird evolved:

Tallest ever	Heaviest ever	Largest predator	Largest flying

Giant moa *Dinornis maximus* 3.7 m (12 ft 1 in)	*Dromornis Dromornis stirtoni* 500 kg (1100 lb)	Terror bird *Phorusrhacos longissimus* 2.5 m (8 ft 3 in) tall	Giant teratorn *Argentavis magnificens* 6 m (20 ft) wingspan
The giant moa lived in New Zealand until relatively recent times. It became extinct soon after the arrival of the first people about 1000 years ago.	*Dromornis* lived in central Australia. It evolved around 15 million years ago and survived until just 25 000 years ago.	Terror birds were the dominant predators in South America until about 2 million years ago, when the land bridge with North America formed, enabling sabretoothed cats to enter the continent.	This prehistoric vulture soared over the pampas of South America between two million and 18 000 years ago. It may have weighed 80 kg (175 lb).

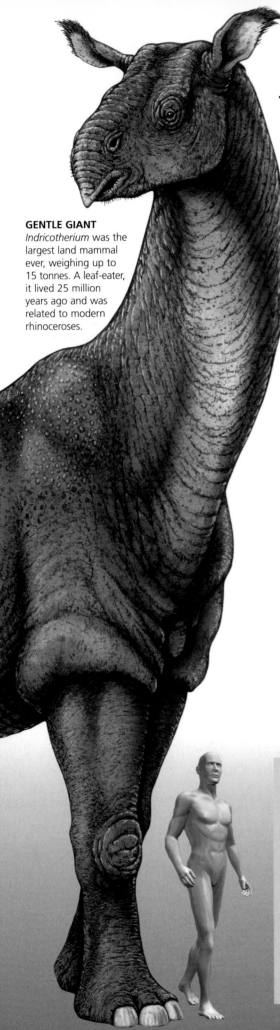

GENTLE GIANT
Indricotherium was the largest land mammal ever, weighing up to 15 tonnes. A leaf-eater, it lived 25 million years ago and was related to modern rhinoceroses.

Ice Age giants ❻

At least four Ice Ages have occurred in the past two million years. The most recent ended 10 000 years ago with the **extinction** of large numbers of creatures, many of them giants. The **woolly rhinoceros** (*Coelodonta antiquus*) and **cave bear** (*Ursus spelaeus*) disappeared at this time; both were much larger than their contemporary equivalents. Another casualty, the **Irish elk** (*Megaloceros*) was the size of a moose but had far bigger antlers, spanning up to 3.7 m (12 ft). **Woolly mammoths** (*Mammuthus primigenius*) survived on isolated Arctic islands until just 4000 years ago, albeit in dwarf form.

WEIRD AND WONDERFUL ❼

At 15 m (50 ft) long, Megalodon was the **biggest predatory shark** ever. Megalodon means 'great tooth' and the name could hardly be more appropriate – some of its now 16-million-year-old teeth are 17 cm (7 in) long.

Polar animals

Lands of snow and ice ❶

◆ North of the **Arctic Circle** trees are replaced by tundra vegetation. Made up of ground-hugging plants, the tundra stretches to the shores of the Arctic Ocean. In winter it is covered with a thick blanket of snow.

◆ Most of **Antarctica** is covered with snow all year round. It has no tundra or equivalent vegetation, no native land mammals and few resident birds. Like the Arctic, most of its inhabitants are migratory and leave as winter closes in.

NORTH POLE
The ice cap floats on the Arctic Ocean, expanding to the shores of Canada, Greenland and Russia in winter.

SOUTH POLE
Antarctica is covered with ice up to three miles thick. The ice sheet stretches out from the land onto parts of the ocean.

North/south divide ❷

Most polar animals are found only in the **Arctic or Antarctic**. However, there are a small number that live in both.

Arctic	Antarctic
Auks	Albatrosses
Beluga	Crabeater seal
Bowhead whale	Giant petrel
Caribou	Humpback whale
Grey whale	Killer whale
Humpback whale	Krill
Killer whale	Leopard seal
Narwhal	Penguins
Polar bear	Ross seal
Walrus	Weddell seal

Summer bounty ❸

◆ The majority of polar animals exist there only for the summer. As the days shorten and the weather worsens, they head off to warmer places.

◆ Although short, polar summers are very productive. With 24-hour sunlight inside the Arctic Circle, tundra plants thrive. Their growth supports an explosion of **small mammals** such as brown lemmings (*Lemmus lemmus*) and huge populations of **breeding birds**.

◆ Summer blooms of **phytoplankton** (algae) in polar waters lead to their own explosions of animal life. In the Antarctic they cause a jump in the numbers of **krill** (*Euphausia superba*) and in the Arctic feed **zooplankton**, which attracts huge shoals of herring (*Clupea harengus*) and other filter-feeding **fish**. These in turn provide food for migratory **seabirds** and **marine mammals** such as grey whales (*Eschrichtius robustus*).

Polar giants ❹

The **largest** species of several creatures are found in the polar regions, including the **blue whale** (*Balaenoptera musculus*) and **southern elephant seal** (*Mirounga leonina*). Large animals retain heat better than small ones as they have a small surface area relative to their volume. The **polar bear** (*Ursus maritimus*) is the largest land-living carnivore; the biggest on record weighed just over a tonne.

Harsh climate and abundant food combine on Alaska's Kodiak island to support the world's biggest **brown bears** (*Ursus arctos*). Although not as large as polar bears they are more bulky, and can weigh 750 kg (1650 lb).

STANDING TALL
Reared up on its back feet, a polar bear may be as much as 3.4 m (11ft 2 in) tall.

610

Winter wardrobes

The **ptarmigan** (*Lagopus mutus*) is one of many creatures to turn white in winter. The **Arctic fox** (*Alopex lagopus*) and **Arctic hare** (*Lepus timidus*) are both brown in summer to help them blend in to a tundra landscape without snow. Other colour changers include the **stoat** (*Mustela erminea*). Its winter coat is all white apart from the black tip of its tail.

Permanent fixtures

A few creatures spend their lives near the poles. The **Arctic fox**, **polar bear** and **bowhead whale** (*Balaena mysticetus*) are found around the Arctic all year, as are several species of seal. In the south, male **emperor penguins** overwinter on the Antarctic ice shelf, brooding eggs laid by mates that spend the winter at sea. Beneath the ice lives the world's **most southerly mammal**, the Weddell seal (*Leptonychotes weddelli*). Weddell seals spend most of their lives underwater but, like all mammals, have lungs and need air. They survive by breathing through holes in the ice which they keep open with their teeth.

5

WHITE WHISTLER
Belugas, or sea canaries, (*Delphinapterus leucas*), live in highly vocal groups of 5–20 animals.

Tie-breaker

6

Q: Which is colder, the Arctic or the Antarctic?
A: The Antarctic is much colder. While temperatures around the North Pole may drop to -62°C (-80°F) at the South Pole they can be as low as -88°C (-126°F).

Surviving the cold **7**

◆ Insects and some fish in polar regions produce **anti-freeze** using glycoproteins, which lowers the temperature at which their bodies would freeze.
◆ Gulls and marine creatures have a **double body-temperature system** to retain heat. Their flippers and feet are able to function at lower temperatures than the rest of their bodies.
◆ Most sea-going birds and mammals have a thick layer of **fat**, or blubber. This provides such efficient insulation that a seal's internal temperature may be 42°C (76°F) higher than its skin temperature.
◆ Polar bears have **black skin**, in addition to a thick coat and a layer of fat. Their hair is transparent but appears white because of the way in which it refracts and reflects light.

122 cm (48 in) **EMPEROR PENGUIN** *Aptenodytes patagonica*
The largest penguin species, and largest marine bird. It breeds on the Antarctic continent in winter.

Antarctica's penguins **8**

Penguins live in the ocean and come ashore to breed. The larger, best insulated species live around Antarctica and sub-Antarctic islands. Smaller species live farther north.

91.5 cm (36 in)

CHINSTRAP PENGUIN
Pygoscelis antarctica
Breeds on the most northerly peninsulas of Antarctica, and on sub-Antarctic islands.

61 cm (24 in)

LITTLE BLUE PENGUIN
Eudyptula minor
The smallest species, the little blue lives off southern Australia and New Zealand.

30.5 cm (12 in)

Forest animals

Taiga to tropics ❶

◆ Forest once covered much of the Earth's land surface and great swathes still exists on every continent apart from Antarctica. There are **three main types** of forest in existence today.

◆ **Tropical rain forest** occurs in the tropics and straddles the Equator. It is the planet's richest habitat, both in terms of number of species and biomass (weight of living matter per unit area).

◆ Bands of **temperate forest** occur north and south of the tropics. In the north the trees are deciduous (drop their leaves in autumn) while in the south they keep their leaves all year round.

◆ **Conifer forest** exists only in the Northern Hemisphere. It extends to the tundra and supports fewer species than other forest types. Conifers keep their needle-like leaves all year.

High-rise homes ❷

Most tree-living animals sleep in the branches, but a few have more permanent homes. **Red squirrels** (*Sciurus vulgaris*) build nests called dreys to spend the night in. **Bats** that hunt insects spend the day hanging upside-down in hollow tree trunks. And various climbing rodents, such as the **common dormouse** (*Muscardinus avellanarius*), curl up in natural holes.

HOMEMAKER Woodpeckers, such as this red-naped sapsucker (*Sphyrapicus varius*), excavate holes to nest in. These later become home to other tree-living animals.

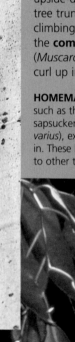

Forests of grass ❸

Bamboo is the world's largest grass, and in south-west China it covers whole hillsides. The most famous resident of China's bamboo forests is the **giant panda** (*Ailuropoda melanoleuca*). It feeds almost exclusively on bamboo, occasionally taking birds and small mammals. The panda shares its home with a rare monkey, the **snub-nosed langur** (*Rhinopithecus roxellanae*), which also eats bamboo.

GETTING A GRIP Unlike bears, the giant panda can grasp with its paws.

Moving through the branches

Life in the trees is very different from down on the ground and most animals have particular **adaptations** to cope with it. Small mammals, such as **squirrels**, have sharply curved claws for gripping bark, while **monkeys** have long palms and fingers for holding on to branches. **Treefrogs** and **geckos** have toes that grip; the former by suction and the latter with microscopic hooks.

FIFTH LIMB Like many climbing animals, South America's spider monkeys have prehensile tails that can wrap around branches.

Eyes front

For fast movement in the trees being able to judge distance is vital. Most active tree-dwelling mammals, such as monkeys, have eyes that look directly forward. This gives them what is known as **binocular vision** – the fields of view of each eye cross over enabling their owner to work out how far away objects are.

Flying without wings

Gliding has evolved in all sorts of animals as a solution to the problem of moving between trees. By gliding, animals can avoid coming down to the ground – where they might be at risk from predators – and span gaps between trees. Gliding animals include the flying frog, flying snakes, flying dragons (lizards) and several species of mammal.

FLYING TONIGHT The sugar glider (*Petaurus breviceps*) lives in Australia and Papua New Guinea. A marsupial, it feeds on insects and nectar.

Life in layers

Most forests have two layers: the branches and the forest floor. Lowland tropical **rain forest**, however, divides up into **five separate layers**, each with its own particular animals. The canopy has the largest number of species, including most fruit-eaters. Emergents provide nest sites and lookout posts for aerial predators such as eagles, while the herb layer is home to creatures that feed mostly on what falls from above. The middle layer and shrub layer support few species of their own but offer safe havens for leaf-eaters, such as sloths, out of reach of most predators. They are also home to opportunist feeders such as marmosets and tamarins, and provide well-hidden nest sites for numerous forest birds.

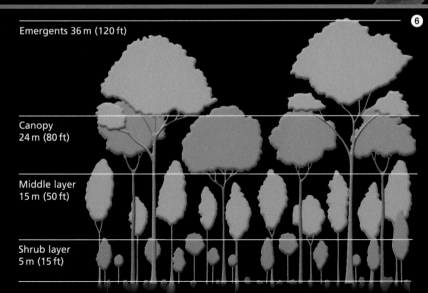

Emergents 36 m (120 ft)

Canopy 24 m (80 ft)

Middle layer 15 m (50 ft)

Shrub layer 5 m (15 ft)

Grassland animals

Where grasslands occur ❶

◆ **Grasslands** separate the planet's deserts from its forest belt. They are characterised by rainfall that is too light to support trees.
◆ Grasslands are home to the world's **largest and fastest** land animals, and also the majority of its pack predators. They provide an abundance of food virtually all year round and are second only to forests in terms of the numbers of animals they support.
◆ The world's **most expansive** grasslands are in Africa, Asia and South America. Grasslands are under threat because of the ease with which they can be turned into farmland. Those in temperate zones are particularly at risk.

HEAVY ARMOUR The two-tonne Indian rhinoceros (*Rhinoceros unicornis*) combines size with thick skin to deter predators.

Bigger is better ❷

The massive size of some of the plant-eaters makes them **invulnerable** to predators and better able to **protect their young** in a habitat where there is virtually no cover. Today's grassland giants are the last remnants from a golden age of mammals. Two million years ago the world's plains were covered with enormous grazers (grass eaters) and browsers (animals that feed on leaves from trees and bushes). Their demise was caused by the onset of the last great Ice Age which saw forests spread and grassland shrink.

Survival of the quickest ❸

Grassland animals include the fastest runners on the planet. In Africa the **cheetah** (*Acionyx jubatus*) reaches speeds of over 96 km/h (60 mph) in pursuit of prey such as the **springbok** (*Antidorcas marsupialis*), which itself can top 90 km/h (55 mph). The **pronghorn** (*Antilocapra americana*) from North America's prairies holds the world speed record over distance (see page 40). Even birds from grasslands reach speeds that put Olympic sprinters in the shade. The fastest of all, the **ostrich** (*Struthio camelus*), can exceed 72 km/h (45 mph).

RUNNING JUMP Many gazelles and antelopes, such as these impala (*Aepyceros melampus*) from southern and eastern Africa, jump to confuse pursuing predators.

GROUP VIOLENCE A spotted hyena separated from its clan is attacked by a pack of African hunting dogs.

Deadly competition ④

Hunting by ambush on plains is much more difficult than in other habitats and **group hunting** has evolved as a result. Competition between group predators is often fierce and on Africa's savannah it is particularly so. **Border disputes** between members of the same species sometimes lead to bloodshed, often death. Lions, (*Panthera leo*), hunting dogs (*Lycaon pictus*) and spotted hyenas (*Crocuta crocuta*) not only steal each others' prey but actually kill each other over it. This aggression may seem extreme but it does have a purpose. By eliminating some of the competition, carnivores improve their chances of keeping their own kills and stealing them from others.

Plain speaking ⑤

Grassland has different names in different parts of the world.

Name	Place
Campos	Brazil
Llanos	Venezuela and Columbia
Pampas	Argentina
Prairie	North America
Savannah	Africa
Steppe	Southeastern Europe and Russia
Veld	South Africa

Termite hordes ⑥

◆ Mention **grazers** and people think of zebras or antelopes, but on most grasslands termites far outweigh their more visible competitors. In one acre of African savannah there might be millions of the little insects, each one hungry for grass.
◆ Termites **provide food** for a wide range of birds and larger animals. In South America the giant anteater (*Mymecophaga tridactyla*) and several species of armadillo live on them, while in India the world's third-largest bear, the sloth bear (*Ursus ursinus*), eats almost nothing else.
◆ The first two animals in the dictionary, the aardvark (*Orycteropus afer*) and aardwolf (*Proteles cristatus*) are both **termite eaters**.

INSECT TOWER BLOCKS Termite mounds dot the Australian outback. Worldwide, termites outweigh humans 10 times to one.

★ 63

Tough grazer

The Cape buffalo (*Syncerus caffer caffer*) is a formidable animal. Standing over 1.5 m (5 ft) at the shoulder and weighing 800 kg (1800 lb), adult bulls charge and often kill attacking lions. Buffaloes are **Africa's only cattle**. A dwarf race, the bush cow (*Syncerus caffer nanus*), lives in the tropical rain forest of western Africa and the Congo Basin.

Tie-breaker ⑦

Q: On the grasslands of which continent would you find a rhea and a maned wolf?
A: South America. The long-legged maned wolf (*Chrysocyon brachyurus*) is a solitary hunter that feeds mostly on rodents. The common rhea (*Rhea americana*) eats grass and insects and is the world's third tallest bird.

The numbers or star following the answers refer to information boxes on the right.

ANSWERS

⭐ **20** **False** ⭐

226 **Erwin Rommel (1891–1944)**

396 **D: Desert** ⑤

409 **True** – dromedary camels have just one hump

631 **A: To keep out sand** – their nostrils close too

632 **D: To help them keep cool** ③

633 **A: In its breast feathers** ④

634 **C: The Arabian oryx** ④

636 **B: To swim through sand** ②

637 **D: By detecting vibrations** ②

638 **B: A rodent** ④

639 **C: Gobi** – extends from Mongolia into China

788 **False** (most are active at night) ③

804 **The Desert Rats** (their emblem was a jerboa) ④

919 **Bactrian camel** – they live mainly in Mongolia

944 **A lizard** – it lives in the deserts of North America

Desert animals

Hot and dry ①

◆ Strictly, deserts are places that get less than 25 cm (10 in) of rain a year. Desert animals are adapted either to go without drinking or to conserve what little water they manage to find.
◆ The majority of deserts are very hot and most desert animals exhibit physical features or behaviours that help them keep cool.

◆ Generally the longer a desert has existed the more species will have adapted to live in it. The world's **oldest desert** is Africa's **Namib** and for its size has more endemic species (species that are found nowhere else) than any other.
◆ The world's **largest desert** is the **Sahara**, followed by the Australian and Arabian deserts.

Sink or swim ②

One way to **avoid predators** is to hide, but there is not much cover in the desert. Some creatures get around this by disappearing into the sand. At the first sign of danger the **American fringe-toed lizard** (*Uma scoparius*) wriggles down between the grains. Conversely, some predators use the sand for cover, lying in wait or 'swimming' through it in search of a meal.

POP-UP PREDATOR A Namib golden mole (*Eremitalpa granti*) feasts on a locust. The mole locates its prey by picking up vibrations through the sand.

Big ears and burrows ③

◆ **Keeping cool** in the desert in daytime is especially difficult for mammals, who, unlike reptiles and invertebrates, generate their own body heat. Small mammals get around this in two ways:
◆ Many, such as North America's **kit fox** (*Vulpes macrotis*) and **black-tailed jackrabbit** (*Lepus californicus*), have large ears that disperse excess heat.
◆ Almost all dig burrows where they shelter from the sun by day. Most small mammals emerge only at night to find food, and predators find their large ears doubly useful, as they help to locate prey in the dark.

RADAR DISHES The fennec fox (*Fennecus zerda*) lives in Arabia and the northern Sahara desert. For its size, it has the largest ears of any carnivore.

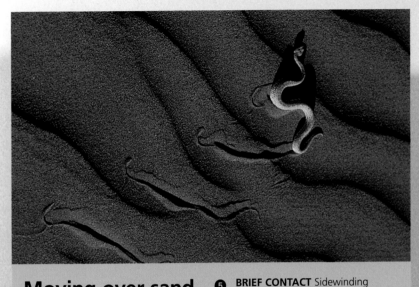

Heavy drinker

A thirsty **dromedary** camel (*Camelus dromedarius*) can drink a third of its own bodyweight in just 10 minutes. Dromedaries' blood cells are egg-shaped but balloon into spheres to soak up a sudden intake of water. The single hump has nothing to do with water storage but acts as a food store of fat.

Life without water ❹

In the desert water is hard to find and animals have evolved ways to cope without it. Some never drink at all, obtaining all the moisture they need from the food that they eat. Most desert reptiles do this but a surprising number of mammals do so as well. Rodents such as Australia's **desert mice**, North America's **kangaroo rats** and African and Asian **jerboas** all survive without water, as do several desert antelopes, including the **addax** (*Addax nasomaculatus*), **Arabian oryx** (*Oryx leucoryx*) and **dorcas gazelle** (*Gazella dorcas*).

Moving over sand ❺

Sand is hard to move across under any conditions, but in the desert by day it is scorching hot too. Because they are most active by day, desert reptiles have had to come up with ways of moving without getting their feet or bodies burned. Some lizards, such as North

BRIEF CONTACT Sidewinding enables desert snakes such as this sidewinder rattlesnake to travel with minimal contact with the hot sand.

America's **gridiron-tailed lizard** (*Callisaurus draconoides*), move quickly between areas of shade by running on their back feet. For footless snakes this is not an option. Two species have hit on sidewinding as a solution – the North American **sidewinder rattlesnake** (*Crotalus cerastes*) and Africa's **horned viper** (*Cerastes cerastes*).

FANCY FOOTWORK The Namib's sand-diving lizard (*Aporosaurus anchietae*) prevents its feet getting burned by alternating which it stands on.

NON-DRINKER Like many other desert antelopes the gemsbok (*Oryx gazella*) can survive without drinking, getting all of the moisture it needs from its food. This animal is in the Namib desert in southwestern Africa.

WEIRD AND WONDERFUL ❻

The **Namib** is one of Earth's driest deserts, but some of its inhabitants manage to drink every day. At night, darkling beetles stand in such a way that fog rolling in off the sea condenses on their bodies and runs into their mouths.

Mountain animals

A head for heights ❶

◆ Mountains offer some of the toughest challenges to survival on land. Thin air, low temperatures and scant vegetation make life for animals very hard indeed.

◆ Numbers of all creatures diminish with altitude. Above the treeline most niches are held by just one kind of animal and there is little competition between species for food. Above the tundra almost no life survives at all.

◆ Movement in the mountains is difficult, particularly for large animals, and only the most agile species can get around. Plant-eaters are much more common than carnivores: most ranges are dominated by sheep and goats.

Tough at the top ❷

Large carnivores are rare in the mountains. The **snow leopard**, or ounce, is the only truly alpine big cat. About the same size as its lowland cousin, it spends the night in dens among the rocks, emerging at dawn to hunt for prey. In North and South America the **puma** (*Felis concolor*) hunts at altitudes of up to 5800 m (16 400 ft). Subspecies of **brown bear** (*Ursus arctos*) occur in mountains throughout Eurasia and North America. South America's only bear, the **spectacled bear** (*Tremarctos ornatus*), lives in the Andes.

RARE BEAUTY Found only in the Himalayas and Mongolia's Altai range, the snow leopard is illegally hunted for its luxuriant pelt. Fewer than 5000 are thought to remain in the wild.

Islands in the sky ❸

Most mountain ranges are isolated and few creatures that evolve on one range ever travel to another. The world's only alpine cattle, **yaks** (*Bos grunniens*) are restricted to the Himalayas, and the **Rocky Mountain goat** (*Oreamnos americanus*) is found only in the range after which it is named. Many animals restricted to one range have relatives in others, however. Europe's **alpine marmot** (*Marmota marmota*) has similar cousins in North America, the hoary marmot (*Marmota caligata*) and yellow-bellied marmot (*Marmota flaviventris*), for example.

Treading carefully ❹

On the flat the dew claws are raised up off the ground

When climbing they are used for extra grip

Sheep and **goats** are almost all mountain-dwellers. **Chamois** (*Rupicapra rupicapra*) inhabit the European ranges along with ibex, which also occur in northeast Africa and the western Himalayas. Siberia and North America are dominated by three subspecies of bighorn sheep (*Ovis canadensis*), while the ranges of central Asia have their own species, such as the **Himalayan tahr** (*Hemitragus jemlahicus*).

FEET FOR GRIPPING Ibex have soft, concave pads on the backs of their feet which they use like suction cups when climbing. These dew claws appear on most cloven-hoofed mammals but, other than ibex, few ever use them.

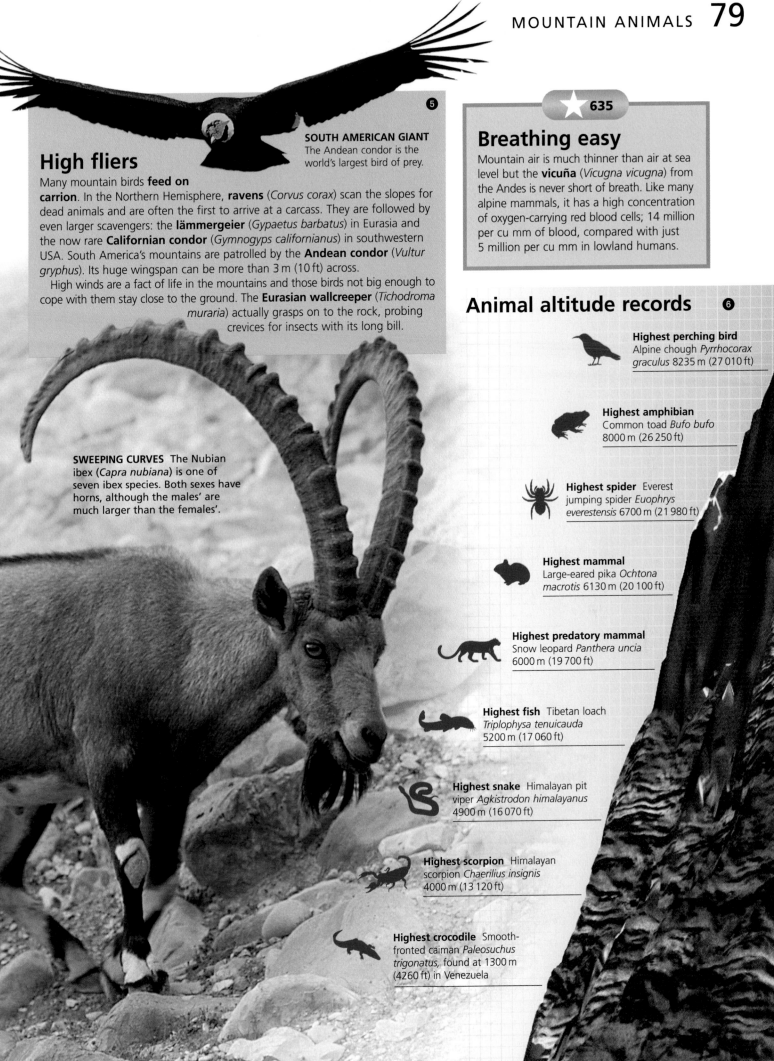

5

SOUTH AMERICAN GIANT
The Andean condor is the world's largest bird of prey.

High fliers

Many mountain birds **feed on carrion**. In the Northern Hemisphere, **ravens** (*Corvus corax*) scan the slopes for dead animals and are often the first to arrive at a carcass. They are followed by even larger scavengers: the **lämmergeier** (*Gypaetus barbatus*) in Eurasia and the now rare **Californian condor** (*Gymnogyps californianus*) in southwestern USA. South America's mountains are patrolled by the **Andean condor** (*Vultur gryphus*). Its huge wingspan can be more than 3 m (10 ft) across.

High winds are a fact of life in the mountains and those birds not big enough to cope with them stay close to the ground. The **Eurasian wallcreeper** (*Tichodroma muraria*) actually grasps on to the rock, probing crevices for insects with its long bill.

★ **635**

Breathing easy

Mountain air is much thinner than air at sea level but the **vicuña** (*Vicugna vicugna*) from the Andes is never short of breath. Like many alpine mammals, it has a high concentration of oxygen-carrying red blood cells; 14 million per cu mm of blood, compared with just 5 million per cu mm in lowland humans.

SWEEPING CURVES The Nubian ibex (*Capra nubiana*) is one of seven ibex species. Both sexes have horns, although the males' are much larger than the females'.

Animal altitude records **6**

Highest perching bird
Alpine chough *Pyrrhocorax graculus* 8235 m (27 010 ft)

Highest amphibian
Common toad *Bufo bufo* 8000 m (26 250 ft)

Highest spider Everest jumping spider *Euophrys everestensis* 6700 m (21 980 ft)

Highest mammal
Large-eared pika *Ochtona macrotis* 6130 m (20 100 ft)

Highest predatory mammal
Snow leopard *Panthera uncia* 6000 m (19 700 ft)

Highest fish Tibetan loach *Triplophysa tenuicauda* 5200 m (17 060 ft)

Highest snake Himalayan pit viper *Agkistrodon himalayanus* 4900 m (16 070 ft)

Highest scorpion Himalayan scorpion *Chaerilius insignis* 4000 m (13 120 ft)

Highest crocodile Smooth-fronted caiman *Paleosuchus trigonatus,* found at 1300 m (4260 ft) in Venezuela

Animals of inland waters

Living in water ❶

◆ The world's inland waters comprise several types of habitat. A wide variety of creatures live in them but most have features in common, many of which they share with marine animals.
◆ Most truly aquatic creatures have **gills** in order to extract oxygen from water.
◆ Most active swimmers have **fins** or **flippers**, while those that spend some time in the water and some out usually have **webbed feet** instead (many also have **flattened tails** to help them swim). While they have much in common, freshwater animals also show great diversity, with adaptations that reflect the particular conditions of where they live.

Islands on land ❷

Standing waters range from tiny ponds to huge inland seas. Much of the life they support is also found in rivers, but some creatures require still water to survive. Most of the world's **amphibians** breed in lakes and ponds, as do many **insects**, including dragonflies, damselflies and water beetles.

Many lakes are completely cut off from other waters and have their own endemic species (species that are found nowhere else). Africa's **Lake Tanganyika** has more than 300 endemic fish, for example, and **Lake Baikal** in Russia has the only exclusively freshwater seal, the Baikal seal (*Pusa sibirica*).

⭐ 212
Winged for a day

Mayflies have the shortest adult lives of any animal. After two years as river-dwelling nymphs, they transform into flying adults, mate and die – all in one day. Mayflies comprise the insect order Ephemeroptera, which actually means 'short-lived wings'.

Rapid flow ❸

Life in a river's upper reaches is a constant battle with the current. **Fish** are either streamlined strong swimmers like the brown trout (*Salmo trutta*), or small enough, like the bullhead (*Cottus gobio*), to shelter among rocks. **Insect larvae** have to hold on tight to avoid being washed away: all have clawed feet, most have flattened bodies, and a few, such as the water penny (a beetle larva), are shaped so that their bodies act as suckers to hold on to rocks.

UNDERWATER WALKER The dipper (*Cinclus cinclus*) hunts insect larvae on the bottom of swift Eurasian streams.

Where river meets sea ❹

At the mouths of many large rivers estuaries form. Dominated by mudflats, these support huge numbers of invertebrates, such as **lugworms**, which in turn provide food for **wading birds**.

Life in the lower reaches

As rivers near the sea they slow down and broaden out. Creatures here tend to be larger than those upstream and a greater variety of species live together. The lower reaches are home to most of the world's 23 crocodilians, including the **alligator** (*Alligator mississippiensis*), and the **caimans** of South America. Other giants include fish such as the Amazon's 2.5 m (8 ft) **pirarucu** (*Arapaima gigas*) and the 3-tonne **common hippo** (*Hippopotamus amphibius*), the world's **largest freshwater mammal**.

RIVER WOLF Called 'lupo rio' in South America where it lives, the giant otter (*Pteronura brasiliensis*) grows to 2.5 m (8 ft) long and is the world's largest otter.

Trees on stilts

In the tropics most deltas and estuaries are covered by **mangroves** – evergreen trees that are tolerant of saltwater. The tidal swamps that form beneath their branches act as nurseries for a wide variety of marine fish and are home to smaller numbers of resident species. **Fiddler crabs** (*Uca* species) are common, as are **mudskipper** fish, which are equally at home in or out of the water.

TRUNK ROUTE Mudskippers clamber up a mangrove sapling. These strange fish have gills but can also absorb oxygen through their skin.

FISH SPECIALIST The rare gharial (*Gavialis gangeticus*) from the Indian subcontinent grows to 6 m (20 ft) long.

Tie-breaker

Q: Which continent do piranhas come from?
A: South America. There are more than 50 species of piranha. Most eat fruit or fish scales, but the infamous red piranha (*Serrasalmus nattereri*) feeds only on flesh. Red piranhas normally hunt fish, but they will kill larger animals. In 1981 red piranhas ate more than 300 people when an overcrowded ferry capsized in Brazil.

Seas and oceans

Earth's biggest habitat ❶

◆ The oceans cover **71 per cent** of the planet's surface and contain a greater variety and mass of life than all the wild areas on land put together. Broadly speaking, they divide up into four regions.

◆ The **shore** is home to the sea's most familiar animals. Most creatures that live here can tolerate short periods out of the water.

◆ **Coastal waters** overlie the continental shelf, up to 500 km (300 miles) from the shore.

◆ Beyond the continental shelf is the **open ocean**. Apart from plankton, inhabitants of the open ocean are relatively few and scattered.

◆ The **deep sea** lies mostly beneath the open ocean. It includes all waters where no light penetrates.

Life in coastal waters ❷

Between the shore and the open ocean are the sea's coastal waters. Relatively shallow, these support the greatest concentrations of marine life, including most of the world's **coral reefs** and the myriad fish and other animals that make the reefs their home. Corals and seaweeds such as kelp thrive here because they are able to harvest the **energy from sunlight** (see also page 87). Farther out, the water gets deeper, so less and less light reaches the bottom. **Coastal mammals** include porpoises and seals. These waters are also the haunt of the **majority of seabirds**, including penguins, auks, cormorants, diving ducks and gulls.

UNDERSEA GARDEN Coral reefs are the most diverse habitat after tropical rain forest. The branching structures on this Australian reef are sea fans – colonies of coral polyps in a flexible skeleton which moves with the currents.

Between the tides

The **shore** is one of the toughest ocean habitats. Creatures that live here must survive being inundated with seawater then dried out by the sun, as well as coping with the regular pounding of waves. Many shore-dwellers are adapted to **cling to rocks**. Some, such as mussels and barnacles, are sessile, that is they spend their whole adult lives anchored to one spot. Others, such as limpets and winkles, move slowly but never release their grip.

Most shore animals are either **filter feeders** or eat filter feeders. A few, such as the shore crab (*Carcinus maenas*), live on what is washed up by the tide.

❸ SEAWEED GRAZER The marine iguana (*Amblyrhynchus cristatus*) is the world's only sea-going lizard.

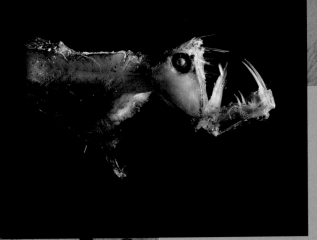

BIG BITE The deep-sea viper fish (*Chauliodus danae*) has a huge mouth and long teeth to grab prey in the dark.

Going deep ④

Below 200 m (650 ft) no sunlight penetrates. The first wavelengths to disappear are reds and most deep sea predators have lost the ability to see this colour. Many creatures that live here are coloured red, effectively making them invisible. To see at these depths some creatures **produce their own light**. Others have huge eyes – the most sensitive of any animal belong to the deep sea crustacean *Gigantocypris*.

⭐ 101

Drifting along

Plankton forms the basis of the **ocean food chain**. The microscopic algae (phytoplankton) that float near the surface produce more oxygen than all land plants put together and provide food for billions of planktonic animals (zooplankton). These in turn sustain filter feeders, from corals to fish, such as anchovies and herring, to the massive blue whale.

Tie-breaker ⑤

Q: In which ocean would you find sockeye salmon?
A: The Pacific. Sockeyes (*Oncorhynchus nerka*) spawn in rivers but spend most of their adult lives at sea. Males are streamlined and silvery, but as they reach breeding condition they turn red and develop a hooked jaw and humped back. After spawning sockeyes die, their bodies enriching the water with nutrients for their offspring.

Wide open spaces ⑥

The **open ocean** is by far the **largest** marine habitat, but it is also the **most barren**. Food is unevenly distributed and rarely stays in one area for long. Animals that live in the open ocean are known as pelagic animals. They are all mobile and many are extremely fast. This habitat contains the **fastest swimming fish** of all, including the sailfish, marlin (*Makaira* species) and the yellowfin tuna (*Thunnus albacares*), all of which have been clocked at over 75 km/h (45 mph).

DECEPTIVELY QUICK
Despite its size, the blue whale (*Balaenoptera musculus*) is one of the fastest swimming mammals, capable of over 30 km/h (20 mph).

Animal classification

The animal family tree ❶

The system of **biological classification** used today was devised in 1758 by the Swedish naturalist Karl von Linné, better known as **Carolus Linnaeus** – the Latin name that he gave to himself. Linné's system has enabled zoologists to draw up a detailed family tree of the animal kingdom which shows how closely related different groups of animals are to each other. Each species is given a **Latin name** which itself tells scientists something about the animal and helps link it to its closest relatives.

Latin names ❷

Every species of animal on Earth has its own Latin name. The name is split into two parts, for example the Latin name for the **tiger** is *Panthera tigris*. The **first half** of the Latin name refers to an animal's genus and is always capitalised. It is shared by all of that animal's closest relatives – in this case the genus name is *Panthera*, which is shared by all big cats. The **second half** of the name is unique to that species. Sometimes it commemorates a scientist or the person who discovered the species, but most often, and most usefully, it gives some information about the animal. The Latin name for the sika deer, *Cervus nippon*, for instance means 'deer from Japan'.

How the tree works ❸

The simplified version of the animal family tree on these pages shows how the major animal groups are related to each other. Animals are split into two main groups, or phyla: the invertebrates and the chordates.

Invertebrates make up 95 per cent of all animals. They include sponges, corals, jellyfish, worms, molluscs, echinoderms, crustaceans, arachnids, myriapods and insects. There are three types of **chordate**: tunicates, lancelets and vertebrates. Almost all chordates alive today are **vertebrates**, which are split into five classes: mammals, birds, reptiles, amphibians and fish.

Chordates

All animals with a spinal cord. Chordates evolved from marine invertebrates about 530 million years ago.

Vertebrates

All vertebrates have a spinal cord and an internal skeleton. About 48 000 species exist.

Birds

Birds have feathers and lay hard-shelled eggs. There are approximately 9000 species.

Reptiles

Reptiles have lungs and scaly skin. There are more than 6000 different species.

Mammals

Mammals feed their young on milk and most have hair. There are over 4000 species.

560

Stuck in the middle

Tunicates and lancelets are neither vertebrates nor invertebrates. Unlike vertebrates they have no bones, but they do have a spinal cord, which separates them from all lower animals. Tunicates and lancelets have survived from a time before vertebrates existed and are reminders of our evolutionary past. There are three types of tunicate alive today: sea squirts, larvaceans and salps. The 20 species of lancelet all resemble fish larvae.

Invertebrates

Invertebrates have no spinal cord and no internal skeleton. Millions of species have been discovered.

Tunicates and lancelets

Chordates without an internal skeleton (see *Stuck in the middle*).

Amphibians

Amphibians have gills when young and lungs as adults. There are about 4000 species.

Fish

Fish have gills and most can breathe only in water. About 25 000 species are known.

Levels of classification

The animal kingdom is split into two phyla. These subdivide into ever smaller groups to identify each creature, as in the example below.

Kingdom
Animalia

Phylum
Chordata

Class
Mammalia

Order
Carnivora

Family
Felidae

Genus
Panthera

Species
Panthera tigris

Subspecies
Panthera tigris altaica

❹ SIBERIAN TIGER *Panthera tigris altaica* is one of eight subspecies of tiger (three are extinct). Only a minority of animals have subspecies.

The five kingdoms of life ❺

All lifeforms on earth belong to one of five kingdoms:
◆ **Animalia:** Animals are lifeforms of more than one cell that can move and must actively take in food to live.
◆ **Protista:** Single-celled organisms that otherwise have the same characteristics as animals make up this kingdom. They include flagellates, ciliates and amoebae.
◆ **Plantae:** Plants make up a kingdom of organisms that generate their own food using energy from the sun.
◆ **Fungi:** Members of the fungi kingdom cannot move like animals or make energy like plants, but must still take in food. They do this by living on or inside a food source.
◆ **Monera:** The simplest lifeforms are single-celled organisms with no cell nucleus, such as bacteria, and they have their own kingdom.

Tie-breaker

❻

Q: Which vertebrates belong to the class Aves?
A: Birds. The word aves is Latin for birds; the singular form of the noun is avis. Avis is the root of several modern words including aviation and avionics.

Simple animals

Bottom of the ladder ❶

◆ The world's **most simple animal** is a sea creature called *Trichoplax adhaerens*. Discovered in aquarium in Austria in 1883, it measures about 3 mm (1/8 in) across and is essentially a tiny pancake of identical cells. Initially *Trichoplax adhaerens* was thought to be the larva of a more complex animal, but in 1971 it was given its own phylum, Placazoa.

◆ One step up from Placazoa is the phylum Porifera, which contains the **sponges**. Like *Trichoplax* and unlike all other animals, sponges have no tissues. They do have distinct layers of cells however, and most have a skeleton of tiny mineral slivers, or spicules. Sponges feed by sucking water through small holes on their surface, filtering it, then pumping it out.

A world of worms ❷

There are more species of worm than there are species of vertebrate – over 65 000 in all. Worms include the **longest animal** on Earth, the boot-lace worm *Lineus longissimus* from the North Sea, which can grow to 55 m (180 ft) long. They also include some of the smallest and most common animals: nematode worms, or roundworms. Eight different phyla contain animals called worms.

Phylum	Common name	Comments
Acanthocephala	Thorny-headed worms or spiny-headed worms	Intestinal parasites that range from 1.5 mm (1/16 in) to 5 m (16 1/2 ft) long. They attach themselves to their host with sharp hooks.
Annelida	Segmented worms	Comprises earthworms, lugworms, ragworms and leeches. The world's biggest leech is the Amazonian species *Haementeria ghilianii*, which can grow to 30 cm (12 in) long.
Aschelminthes	Roundworms and horsehair worms	This phylum also contains creatures such as rotifers, not considered to be worms. Roundworms include parasitic and non-parasitic species. Horsehair worms are parasitic as juveniles but free-living as adults.
Echiuroidea	Echiuroid worms	Mud-burrowing marine worms with a long, mobile proboscis for seizing prey, such as small fish.
Nemertina	Ribbon worms	Open water marine animals.
Pentastomeda	Tongue worms	Live in the nasal passages and lungs of vertebrates. Most occur in the tropics.
Platyhelminthes	Flatworms	Includes free-living flatworms, tapeworms and flukes. Free-living flatworms have amazing powers of regeneration; an individual cut in half will grow into two new animals. Flukes and **tapeworms** are parasitic. Tapeworms may reach 12 m (40 ft) long.
Sipunculoidea	Peanut worms	Exclusively marine. Most live in burrows in sand or mud.

CLEAR KILLER A deadly sea wasp off the coast of Australia. All jellyfish are 95 per cent water.

Jellyfish ❸

◆ Jellyfish have their **own class** in the animal kingdom, **Scyphozoa**, although they belong to the **same phylum** as corals and sea anemones, **Cnidaria**. There are around 200 species of jellyfish. They **start life** as polyps, attached to rocks and other solid surfaces and later develop into their **free-floating adult** forms, known as medusae.

◆ All jellyfish have tentacles that carry stinging cells to kill prey. The **most venomous** is the sea wasp, or box jellyfish (*Chironex fleckeri*), which occurs off northern Australia and parts of Southeast Asia. In Australia it has killed more humans than sharks and crocodiles combined.

WAITING FOR A MEAL Sea anemones extend their tentacles to capture prey – if attacked they pull them inwards.

Sea anemones ❹

◆ There are around 4000 species of sea anemones. They range in size from a few centimetres to more than a metre across. Sea anemones occur from the poles to the tropics, mostly in coastal waters. Anchored in sand or attached to rocks, they survive by catching fish and other creatures in their tentacles, which are armed with stinging cells called nematocysts. Sea anemones belong to the same class as corals, Anthozoa.

◆ Like corals, sea anemones can reproduce either sexually – with eggs and sperm – or asexually. In asexual reproduction a tiny clone buds off from the animal and grows into an identical replica.

 973

Giant worms

The world's **biggest earthworms** average 1.36 m (4 ft 6 in) in length and grow up to 2 cm (³⁄4 in) across; they may reach 6.7 m (22 ft) long. These giant earthworms (*Microchaetus rappi*) hail from South Africa.

Tie-breaker

❻

Q: Which floating hunter is named after an old-fashioned battleship?
A: Portuguese man-of-war. Although it looks like a jellyfish the Portuguese man-of-war (*Physalia physalis*) is actually a community of different simple animals (cnidarians). One forms the float, while others digest food, sting prey or are involved in reproduction.

Corals and coral reefs ❺

Coral reefs are huge communities of tiny individual animals called **coral polyps**, which catch plankton in their tentacles. Most coral polyps secrete chalky shells around their bodies for protection and it is these, massed together, that form the reefs.

Polyps on tropical reefs have millions of single-celled **algae** living inside them. These algae use sunlight to photosynthesise carbohydrates, which supplement the polyps' diet. Until recently it was thought that all reef-building corals were restricted to waters shallow enough for sunlight to penetrate to support algae. But in the 1990s huge reefs were found at the bottom of the north Atlantic, built by polyps with no symbiotic algae at all.

BACKGROUND PICTURE Coral reefs are made from the limestone skeletons of hard corals. Soft corals, another type of coral, live solitary lives and do not secrete limestone.

SEEN FROM SPACE Corals are the only animals to create land. These islands in the Pacific Ocean are all the work of hard corals, as is Australia's famous Great Barrier Reef.

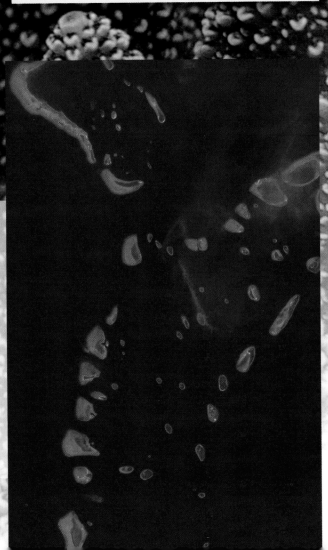

Molluscs and starfish

Core facts ❶

◆ There are more than 50 000 species of **mollusc**, which make up the phylum Mollusca. **Starfish** belong to the phylum Echinodermata.
◆ **Molluscs**, such as mussels, are invertebrates with highly developed blood and nervous systems. They have soft, unsegmented bodies and reproduce sexually.

◆ Most molluscs are covered by an outer layer called the mantle which produces the mineral calcium carbonate, forming a shell.
◆ **Echinoderms**, such as starfish, are the only animals built on a five-part body plan with no head. They have chalky plates just under their skin. Most species can move, but only slowly.

Cockles to cuttlefish

Molluscs are the **most varied group** in the animal kingdom. With no supporting skeleton they have no fixed body shape and have evolved into a huge range of forms.

Among the most simple are **the bivalves**. Aquatic, with two shells hinged together, they include clams, mussels and oysters. Most are sessile (fixed to one place) filter feeders. A few, such as scallops, live unattached to anything, and can move backwards through the water by suddenly clapping their shells shut.

The most familiar molluscs are the **gastropods**, which include slugs and snails. They move slowly on one enormous foot, and feed by means of a rasping tongue, or radula. **Cephalopods** are the most advanced invertebrates. This group contains cuttlefish, squid and octopuses, all of which display complex behaviour. Cephalopods have tentacles covered on one side with suction pads. Octopuses have eight tentacles, squid and cuttlefish 10.

❷

YOUNG GIANT
The Atlantic giant squid (*Architeuthis dux*) is the world's largest invertebrate. This 3 m (10 ft) long specimen was caught by a trawler off the Scottish coast.

What those names mean ❸

Term	Meaning
Bivalve	'Twin shell'. Bivalve molluscs include mussels and scallops
Cephalopod	'Head foot'
Echinoderm	'Spiny skin'
Gastropod	'Stomach foot'. Slugs and snails are gastropods, as are winkles and limpets
Nudibranch	'Naked gills'

Tie-breaker ❹

Q: Which bivalve molluscs produce the finest pearls?
A: Oysters. Pearls form around grains of sand that get stuck inside the shell. Most bivalve molluscs can produce pearls. The world's largest natural pearl, weighing 6.4 kg (14 lb 2 oz), was made by a giant clam (*Tridacna derasa*).

Hermaphrodites and sex-changers ❺

All molluscs reproduce sexually, but some double the chances of passing on their genes by being both male and female at the same time (hermaphrodites). Gastropods make up four-fifths of all mollusc species and many of them are hermaphrodites, including the **garden snail** (*Helix aspersa*).

Some molluscs, such as the **common limpet** (*Patella vulgata*) start life as males but later become female. The rationale behind this is that larger individuals are able to produce more eggs than smaller ones but being small has little effect on the amount of sperm that can be generated.

ONE-FOOT WONDER
The African giant snail (*Achatina achatina*) is the largest land-living mollusc. The biggest individual ever measured was 39 cm (15½ in) long.

Stars and spikes ❻

◆ There are five classes of **echinoderm** – starfish, brittle stars, sea cucumbers, sea urchins and sea lilies.
◆ **Starfish** have thick arms radiating out from a central disc. They move by means of tube feet, and most are carnivorous.
◆ **Brittle stars** have arms that are much thinner than the central disc they radiate from. Most are plankton feeders, although some feed on decaying matter – as do **sea cucumbers**.
◆ **Sea urchins** are omnivorous, move on tube feet and are covered with spines.
◆ Most **sea lilies** are filter feeders living attached to the sea bed.

WEIRD AND WONDERFUL ❼

Among the **most colourful** molluscs are the sea slugs, or **nudibranchs**, found in the tropics. Shell-less gastropods, they protect themselves with stinging cells from their cnidarian prey, which they transfer undigested into

★ 765

Gut reaction

Sausage-shaped creatures that creep over the sea floor, **sea cucumbers** look defenceless. But any predator foolish enough to attack one is in for a surprise. When provoked, a sea cucumber turns its rear end towards its tormentor and squirts a tangle of sticky threads all over them out of its anus.

Coral killers ❽

For the past few decades the Great Barrier Reef and other coral reefs in the Indo-Pacific have been under attack from swarms of starfish. The 40 cm (16 in) diameter **crown-of-thorns starfish** (*Acanthaster planci*) is a natural predator of coral, and some biologists believe that these outbreaks are part of a natural cycle. Others put them down to human interference: the crown-of-thorns' main predator is the giant triton (*Charonia tritonis*), a gastropod mollusc which has been seriously reduced in numbers by shell collectors.

WELL ARMED The crown-of-thorns is covered with poisonous spines.

Insects

Core facts ❶

◆ Insects are the most successful animals on Earth: more than a **million species** have so far been identified.
◆ All insects have certain features in common. They all have a pair of **antennae** and three pairs of mouthparts.

◆ **Insect bodies** are divided into three parts: head, thorax and abdomen. The thorax, in turn, consists of three sections, each with one pair of legs. The abdomen comprises 11 segments with no legs.
◆ Most insects have two pairs of **wings**.

Insect facts and figures ❷

Longest	Heaviest	Smallest	Fastest (on land)
Giant stick insect *Pharnacia kirbyi* 33 cm (13 in)	Goliath beetle *Goliathus goliathus* 100 g (3¹/₂ oz)	Battledore-wing fairy flies family Mymaridae 0.2 mm (⁸/₁₀₀ in)	American cockroach *Periplaneta americana* 5.4 km/h (3¹/₂ mph)

BEEKEEPING TRADITION Today's apiculturists continue a practice that began in ancient Egypt.

Insects and people ❸

The class **Insecta** includes some species that are beneficial to humans but many more that are destructive. **Bees** make honey, for example, and **mulberry silkmoth** (*Bombyx mori*) caterpillars silk. Yet **granary weevils** (*Sitophilus granarius*) decimate grain stores while **clothes moths** (*Tineola bisselliella*) ruin wool and fur.

Insects make up the vast majority of agricultural pests and many, such as **woodworm** (*Anobium punctatum*), **deathwatch beetle** (*Xestobium rufovillosum*) and **drywood termites** (*Incisitermes minor*), damage furniture and buildings.

Taking flight ❹

Insects were the **first animals to fly**. The oldest fossils of flying insects date back more than 350 million years – just 50 million years after animals first emerged onto land. Among the early insects was the **largest flying insect ever**, *Meganeura monyi*, a dragonfly with a 75 cm (30 in) wingspan.

Almost all of today's insects have wings, including earwigs, cockroaches, grasshoppers, mantises and beetles. The **fastest flying insect** is an Australian dragonfly called *Austrophlebia costalis*, which can reach 58 km/h (36 mph) in short bursts.

★ 705

On the run

Anyone who has come across a **cockroach** knows how quick they are. These speedy insects can cover 50 bodylengths in a second – the equivalent of a human sprinting at 330 km/h (205 mph). At top speed a cockroach uses only its two hind legs to run, with the front of its body lifted up in the air.

Altered states ❺

All insects change form at some point in their lifetime; this change is known as **metamorphosis**. **Butterflies**, for example, change almost beyond recognition, forming a chrysalis around themselves as caterpillars and pupating into winged adults. **Beetles** such as ladybirds go through the same process (illustrated).

Different types of insect larvae have different names. Aquatic larvae with legs are called **nymphs**; ant, bee, wasp and (legless) beetle larvae are **grubs**; and fly larvae are **maggots**.

The winged adult may live for a year or more

After three weeks the larva attaches itself to a leaf or stem and starts to pupate

Ladybirds lay about 200 eggs

Each hatches into a wingless larva

Unwitting killers ❻

Some of the world's most deadly diseases are transmitted by insects.

Disease	Carrier
Bubonic plague	Rat flea *Nosopsyllus fasciatus*
Malaria	Malarial mosquitoes *Anopheles* species
Sleeping sickness	Tsetse fly *Glossina* species
Yellow fever	Yellow fever mosquitoes *Aedes* species

All-conquering beetles ❼

A third of all insect species are beetles – more than 370 000 have been discovered so far. They range in size from giants like South America's hercules beetle (*Dynastes hercules*) – at 19 cm (7½ in) the world's longest beetle – to 'feather-winged' beetles (family Ptiliidae), smaller than this full stop.

Beetles live in virtually every land and freshwater habitat. The only places where they are not found are the oceans and polar icecaps. The most successful beetles are the weevils (family Curculionidae) with over 60 000 species – more than all of the land-living vertebrates put together.

QUITE A HANDFUL The goliath beetle weighs more than three times as much as a house mouse, and is eight million times heavier than the smallest beetle.

DESERT SWARM ❾
Desert locusts (*Schistocerca gregaria*) are among the most destructive of insects. Like their cousin, the migratory locust, they swarm in response to sudden plant growth after heavy rainfall.

Tie-breaker

Q: How old was the world's longest-lived insect? ❽
A: 47 years. A golden jewel beetle (*Buprestis aurulenta*), it emerged from the timber of a staircase built 47 years earlier in a house in Southend-on-Sea, England. The golden jewel beetle is found only in North America and the staircase was built from imported pine. The beetle lived for just a few months after emerging.

Arachnids and myriapods

Core facts ❶

◆ Like crustaceans and insects, arachnids and myriapods all belong to the class **Arthropoda** – invertebrates with a tough outer skeleton.
◆ **Arachnids' bodies** are divided into two parts. The front part, or prosoma, carries two pairs of appendages – the pedipalps and chelicerae – and four pairs of legs.

◆ Most arachnids are aggressive predators that prey on other arthropods. Arachnids include spiders, scorpions, mites and ticks.
◆ **Myriapods** include centipedes and millipedes. They have one pair of antennae and a body of many segments. Centipedes have one pair of legs per segment, millipedes have two pairs.

Arachnid facts and figures ❷

Spiders

Largest (legspan)	Smallest (legspan)
Goliath bird-eating spider	Taï Forest midget spider
Theraphosa leblondi	*Anapistula caecula*
9 cm (3½ in)	0.46 mm (1/55 in)

Scorpions

Longest	Shortest
Indian giant scorpion	*Microbothus pusillus*
Heterometrus swannerdami	1.3 cm (1/2 in)
29 cm (11½ in)	

Myriapod facts and figures ❹

Centipedes

Longest	Most legs
Andaman giant centipede	*Himantarum gabrielis*
Scolopendra morsitans	354
33 cm (13 in)	

Millipedes

Longest	Most legs
African giant millipede	Californian siphonophor
Graphidostreptus gigas	*Illacme plenipes*
28 cm (11 in)	750

Centipedes and millipedes ❺

Myriapod means 'many feet' and centipedes and millipedes have more than any other animal. The fewest any millipede has is 24 and all centipedes have at least 15 pairs. Millipede means '1000 legs' and centipede '100 legs'. No millipede actually has 1000 legs and very few centipedes have exactly 100. Millipedes feed only on plant matter but centipedes are active hunters. The fastest is the house centipede (*Scutigera coleoptrata*) from southern Europe, which can reach 1.8 km/h (1.1 mph).

Jaws and pincers

Scorpions and sun spiders occur in the tropics. **Sun spiders** are not spiders at all but belong to their own order, Solifugae. Their mouthparts are the largest of any land-living invertebrate, giving them the strongest bite relative to body size in the animal kingdom.

Like sun spiders, scorpions are active hunters. They capture prey with their pincers and, if necessary, paralyse or kill it with poison from the sting on the end of their tail. The articulated tail and sting is what differentiates true scorpions from their close relatives whip scorpions and pseudoscorpions.

MIGHTY BITE Sun spiders are the fastest land invertebrates, capable of running at 16 km/h (10 mph). ❸

LEFT ALONE Giant millipedes, such as this Madagascan species (below), live above ground and avoid being eaten by exuding a noxious fluid if attacked. Many smaller myriapods live in the soil.

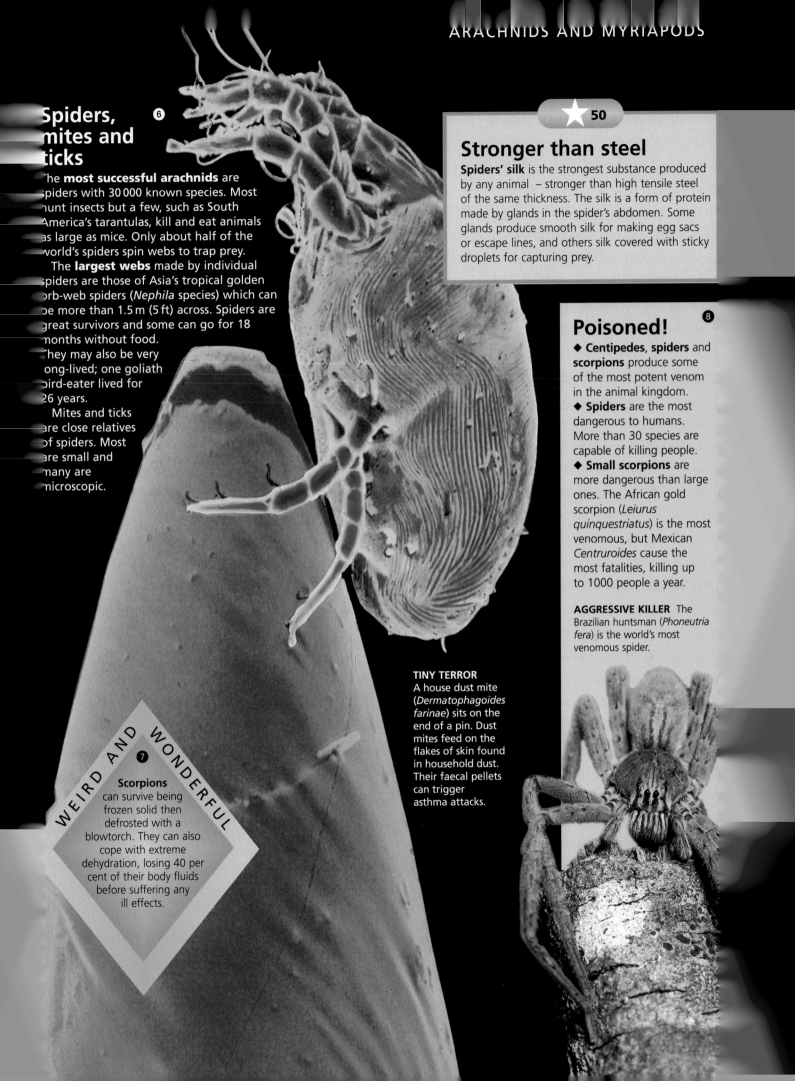

Spiders, mites and ticks ❻

The **most successful arachnids** are spiders with 30 000 known species. Most hunt insects but a few, such as South America's tarantulas, kill and eat animals as large as mice. Only about half of the world's spiders spin webs to trap prey.

The **largest webs** made by individual spiders are those of Asia's tropical golden orb-web spiders (*Nephila* species) which can be more than 1.5 m (5 ft) across. Spiders are great survivors and some can go for 18 months without food. They may also be very long-lived; one goliath bird-eater lived for 26 years.

Mites and ticks are close relatives of spiders. Most are small and many are microscopic.

★ 50

Stronger than steel

Spiders' silk is the strongest substance produced by any animal – stronger than high tensile steel of the same thickness. The silk is a form of protein made by glands in the spider's abdomen. Some glands produce smooth silk for making egg sacs or escape lines, and others silk covered with sticky droplets for capturing prey.

Poisoned! ❽

◆ **Centipedes, spiders** and **scorpions** produce some of the most potent venom in the animal kingdom.
◆ **Spiders** are the most dangerous to humans. More than 30 species are capable of killing people.
◆ **Small scorpions** are more dangerous than large ones. The African gold scorpion (*Leiurus quinquestriatus*) is the most venomous, but Mexican *Centruroides* cause the most fatalities, killing up to 1000 people a year.

AGGRESSIVE KILLER The Brazilian huntsman (*Phoneutria fera*) is the world's most venomous spider.

TINY TERROR
A house dust mite (*Dermatophagoides farinae*) sits on the end of a pin. Dust mites feed on the flakes of skin found in household dust. Their faecal pellets can trigger asthma attacks.

WEIRD AND WONDERFUL ❼

Scorpions can survive being frozen solid then defrosted with a blowtorch. They can also cope with extreme dehydration, losing 40 per cent of their body fluids before suffering any ill effects.

Crustaceans and relatives

Core facts

◆ A crustacean is any member of the invertebrate class Crustacea, the **second largest class** in the animal kingdom after insects.
◆ Most crustaceans are **aquatic** but a few, such as woodlice, live on land.
◆ Crustaceans have two pairs of antennae and three pairs of mouthparts.
◆ Their bodies are divided into a head, thorax and abdomen, although the head and thorax are usually fused.
◆ Many crustaceans have oval, unsegmented **larvae** known as nauplius larvae.

Crustacean facts and figures ❷

Largest (legspan)	Heaviest	Smallest	Fastest (on land)
Japanese spider crab	North Atlantic lobster	Water flea	Ghost crab
Macrocheira kaempferi	*Homarus americanus*	*Alonella* species	*Ocypode* species
3.7 m (12 ft 2 in)	20 kg (44 lb 1 oz)	0.25 mm ($^{1}/_{1000}$ in)	7 km/h ($4^{1}/_{2}$ mph)

Edible crustaceans ❸

Restaurant menus are full of crustaceans, but of the 38 000 known species, just a few dozen are eaten. The **edible crab** (*Cancer pagurus*) and **European lobster** (*Homarus vulgaris*) are among the most familiar. Other examples include **crayfish**, which look like lobsters but live in fresh water, **tiger prawns** (*Penaeus* species), and the **langoustine**, or Norway lobster (*Nephrops norvegicus*).

BEACH PARTY Unlike marine crustaceans, which lay their eggs in water, horseshoe crabs come out of the sea to spawn on land.

Living fossils

Close relatives of arachnids and crustaceans but actually neither, **horseshoe crabs** or king crabs have survived virtually unchanged for more than 150 million years. Although only five species now exist, they have their own class – Merostomata, meaning 'segmented mouths'.

★ 99

Woodlice

Woodlice are the most successful of all land-living crustaceans. Remarkably, they have gills instead of lungs and must remain damp to survive. Woodlice feed on plant remains and live in leaf litter and under rotting logs. The females carry their eggs around in a pouch on the underside of their bodies. Young woodlice hatch fully formed.

EXTERNAL NOSTRILS Woodlice use their antennae not as feelers but to pick up scent.

The pincer movement ❺

Crabs, **lobsters** and **prawns** are grouped into the family Decapoda, which literally means 'ten feet'. Crabs and most lobsters actually have eight feet; the ninth and tenth limbs end in pincers.

◆ **Lobsters** live in the sea and include the **fastest crustaceans** of all; large members of the genus *Palinurus* can leap backwards at 29 km/h (18 mph) to escape predators.

◆ Unlike lobsters, most **crabs** cannot walk forwards because of the way that their legs join their bodies. Instead they scuttle sideways.

◆ **Prawns** are the most numerous decapods. Most are marine but a few live in fresh water.

WEIRD AND WONDERFUL ❻

Some **mantis shrimps** (*Squilla* species) club prey to death with a lightning fast punch. Their punch is so powerful that aquarists cannot keep them – the shrimps simply break through the glass of their tanks and escape.

On land and sea ❽

Crustaceans have colonised virtually every habitat on Earth. They can be found in the deepest parts of the ocean and the middle of its driest deserts. Red shrimps and amphipods exist on the floor of the Marianas Trench, 10 900 m (35 750 ft) down, for example, while the marsupial crab and tadpole shrimps (*Triops* species) live in the scorching Australian outback.

Insects may be much more numerous in terms of species and individual numbers, but crustaceans outweigh them when it comes to the sheer overall mass. Shrimp-like **krill** (*Euphausia superba*), for example, underpin the entire Antarctic ecosystem, feeding everything from fish and penguins to the world's largest whales.

ISLAND CLIMBER The robber, or coconut, crab (*Birgus latro*, main picture) from the Indo-Pacific can weigh more than 4 kg (9 lb), making it the world's largest land-living crustacean.

Tie-breaker

❼
Q: Which crustaceans stick to whales and the hulls of ships?
A: Barnacles. Barnacles were once thought to be molluscs, but in fact they are more closely related to crabs than to clams. Barnacles attach themselves by the head to other objects and use their feathery legs to filter food from the water.

Fish 1

Core facts ❶

◆ Fish are split into **three separate classes**. The first class, Agnatha, contains the jawless fish, which are the most primitive vertebrates. The second class, Chondrichthyes, contains the cartilaginous fish, which include all sharks, rays and ratfish. The third class, Osteichthyes, contains the bony fish. All fish can breathe in water and have fins rather than legs.

◆ **Jawless fish** have no scales or jaws. Their gill openings are circular and their mouths sucker-like and studded with small, sharp teeth.

◆ **Cartilaginous fish** have small, toothlike scales and skeletons made of cartilage with reinforcing mosaics of small, bony plates. Like jawless fish and unlike bony fish, they have no swim bladder.

◆ **Bony fish** are the most numerous fish and also the most successful vertebrates. They have skeletons of bone and most breathe with gills. Garpikes (order Semionotiformes), snakeheads (order Channiformes), lungfish (order Dipnoi) bichirs (order Polypteriformes), and swamp eels (order Synbranchiformes) have primitive lungs.

Fish facts and figures

❷

Whale shark 18 m (59 ft)

Cartilaginous fish

Longest	Heaviest	Shortest	Fastest
Whale shark	Whale shark	Spined pygmy shark	Shortfin mako shark
Rhincodon typus	*Rhincodon typus*	*Squaliolus laticaudus*	*Isurus oxyrinchus*
18 m (59 ft)	21 tonnes (20.7 tons)	25 cm (9³/4 in)	88.5 km/h (55 mph)

Bony fish

Longest	Heaviest	Shortest	Fastest
Oarfish	Sunfish	Dwarf goby	Cosmopolitan sailfish
Regalecus glesne	*Mola mola*	*Trimmatom nanus*	*Istiophorus platypterus*
17 m (57 ft)	2235 kg (4927 lb)	8.8 mm (¹/3 in)	109 km/h (68 mph)

Jawless fish ❸

There are just **45 living species** of jawless fish. **Hagfish** live on the seabed in waters outside the tropics. Although efficient scavengers, often the first to arrive at a corpse, they are also active hunters, seeking out marine invertebrates at night. Hagfish have only tiny, sightless eyes and find their food using sensitive tentacles around their mouths.

The other type of jawless fish, **lampreys**, are parasites, attaching themselves to other fish and rasping through their flesh to drain their blood.

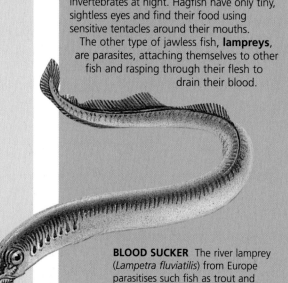

BLOOD SUCKER The river lamprey (*Lampetra fluviatilis*) from Europe parasitises such fish as trout and salmon.

All about sharks ❹

Sharks are the most successful predators in the sea. There are 368 species inhabiting virtually every marine habitat from coral reefs to polar waters, from open ocean to the deep sea. A few species live in brackish water and two inhabit rivers: the **Ganges shark** (*Glyphis gangeticus*) lives in India's Ganges and Hooghly rivers, while the **bull shark** (*Carcharhinus leucas*) occurs in large rivers linked to tropical or subtropical seas worldwide, including the Amazon, Zambezi and Mississippi.

Sharks include the biggest living animals after whales. The **largest species**, the whale shark, feeds entirely on plankton, but virtually all other species are active hunters. Most sharks have extremely acidic stomach juices and can digest almost anything, including bone. Some, such as **tiger sharks** (*Galeocerdo cuvier*) have a tendency to swallow inanimate objects.

★ 896

Toothless giant

Like its cousin the whale shark, the 10 m (33 ft) long **basking shark** (*Cetorhinus maximus*), is a toothless plankton feeder. Basking sharks live in cooler water than whale sharks and occur off the coast of Britain.

Shark attacks ❺

Of the 368 species of shark 42 have been recorded as **attacking people** – 33 unprovoked (below) – and 11 as killing them. Studies of victims of shark attacks have shown that in around three-quarters of all cases the wounds inflicted were so-called 'keep your distance' bites rather than serious feeding attempts.

Shark	Attacks	Fatalities
Great white	254	67
Tiger	83	29
Bull	69	17
Sand tiger	39	2
Blacktip	26	0
Requiem	22	5
Hammerhead	18	0
Blue	15	3
Blacktip reef	14	0
Shortfin mako	13	2
Spinner	13	0
Lemon	10	0
Caribbean reef	10	0
Bronze whaler	9	0
Nurse	8	0
Grey reef	7	0
Sandbar	5	0
Sevengill	5	0
Ocean whitetip	4	0
Wobbegong	4	0
Dusky	3	1
Leopard	3	1
Silky	2	0
Whitetip reef	2	0
Silvertip	2	0
Galapagos	1	1
Ganges	1	1
Tope	1	0
Cookiecutter	1	0
Mako	1	0
Porbeagle	1	0
Scalloped hammerhead	1	0
Spiny dogfish	1	0

Records collated from 1580–2000

WIDE EYED The scalloped hammerhead shark (*Sphyrna lewini*) can exceed 4 m (13 ft) long but rarely attacks people. Schools of this species may be hundreds strong.

Skates and rays ❻

There are more than 400 species of skates and rays. Like sharks, the largest species swim in open water and feed on plankton. The largest of all – the **manta ray** (*Manta birostris*) – lives in tropical marine waters and may measure 7 m (23 ft) from the tip of one wing-like pectoral fin to the other.

Most skates and rays are predators, and some use electricity to kill prey. The **Atlantic torpedo ray** (*Torpedo nobiliana*) can give a shock of 220 volts. Skates and rays include many unusual creatures such as **sawfish** (*Pristis* spp) and **guitarfish** (*Rhina* spp). Skates' and rays' gill slits are on the underside of the body.

STING IN THE TAIL The southern stingray (*Dasyatis americana*) lives in coastal waters from New Jersey to Brazil. It may reach 1.5 m (5 ft) across.

Fish 2

Fish on the menu ❶

Fish	Place of origin	Additional information
Anchovy *Engraulis* species	Central Atlantic, southeastern Pacific and Indian Oceans	Small open water fish that forms huge shoals
Atlantic salmon *Salmo salar*	Arctic and north Atlantic; adjoining rivers and lakes	Spawns in fresh water; farmed in Scotland, Norway, Canada and Chile
Cod *Gadus morhua*	North Sea, northeastern Atlantic, northeastern Pacific	Bottom-living fish found as deep as 600 m (2000 ft)
Dover sole *Solea solea*	Mediterranean, eastern Atlantic including English Channel	Flatfish; named after the Strait of Dover, where it is commonly caught
Haddock *Melanogrammus aeglefinus*	North Sea, northern Atlantic	Bottom-living: second only to cod in importance to Atlantic fishing
Halibut *Hippoglossus hippoglossus*	North Sea, northern Atlantic	Deep-water species; largest flatfish growing to 2.5 m (8 ft 4 in) long
Herring *Clupea harengus*	North Atlantic	Smoked herrings are called kippers
Mackerel *Scomber* species	Indian Ocean, Atlantic, Pacific	Shoaling, open water fish
Monkfish *Lophius* species	Northern Atlantic Ocean	Deep-sea bottom-dwelling fish, also known as anglerfish
Plaice *Pleuronectes platessa*	Mediterranean, eastern Atlantic Ocean from Morocco to Iceland	Most common North Atlantic commercial flatfish
Rainbow trout *Salmo gairdneri*	Rivers, lakes and coastal waters around the world	From western North America, introduced to many other countries
Red snapper *Lutjanus campechanus*	Caribbean Sea, Gulf of Mexico, western central Atlantic Ocean	Farmed commercially off Puerto Rico
Rock salmon or **flake** *Squalus acanthius*	Temperate and cold ocean waters worldwide	World's most common shark, also known as the spiny dogfish
Sardine or **pilchard** *Sardina pilchardus*	European coastal waters	Sardine is the term for the young; pilchard is used for fully-grown fish
Sea bass *Dicentrarchus labrax*	Mediterranean, eastern Atlantic from Morocco to Scotland	May reach 1 m (3 ft 4 in) long
Skate *Raja batis*	Northern North Sea and the waters off Iceland	Largest and heaviest European ray, weighing up to 113 kg (250 lb)
Swordfish *Xiphias gladius*	Warm oceans worldwide	Solitary open water hunter that may reach 4.9 m (16 ft 4 in) long
Trout *Salmo trutta*	Rivers, lakes and coastal waters around northern Europe	Known as brown trout when in fresh water and sea trout when at sea
Tuna *Thunnus* species	Warm seas worldwide	Streamlined, predatory shoaling fish. Largest (northern bluefin *Thunnus thynnus*) may exceed 700 kg (1540 lb)
Turbot *Scophthalmus maximus*	Mediterranean and Black Seas, eastern Atlantic Ocean	Flatfish

THE WELS
This giant catfish lives in rivers across Europe.

The cat's whiskers ❷

Catfish make up a tenth of all known species of fish and have an almost worldwide distribution. Named for the sensitive, whisker-like barbels that protrude from around their mouths, they are mostly bottom-dwelling hunters and scavengers that rely on touch to find their food. The majority of catfish live in freshwater habitats, and this group includes the **largest freshwater fish** of all – the wels (*Silurus glanis*). One example, caught in Russia's Dnieper River in the 19th century, weighed 336 kg (720 lb) and measured 4.6 m (15 ft) long.

Flatfish ❸

◆ Flatfish look like most fish do after they have been filleted. While most fish move their bodies so that their tails sweep from side to side, flatfish undulate theirs so that their tails move up and down.

◆ Flatfish larvae start life looking quite normal, but as they grow one of their eyes migrates until both lie on the same side of their head.

◆ Flatfish are all bottom-living marine predators. Most are well-camouflaged and many can change colour. They catch their prey by lying in wait, often covered by a thin layer of mud or sand with only their eyes visible.

Fish out of water ❹

Many surface fish jump to escape predators but a few actually take to the air. Some species of **flying fish** (family Exocoetidae) can remain aloft for up to 40 seconds, gliding as far as 400 m (1310 ft) before re-entering the water. **Flying gurnards** (order Dactylopteriformes) can also travel for long distances over the waves, as can the **flying halfbeak** (*Euleptorhamphus velox*). All of these fish live in tropical seas and glide by means of enlarged pectoral fins, held against the body when swimming but spread wide as soon as the fish leaves the water.

400 m (1310 ft)

Eels ❺

◆ With their long, sinuous bodies, eels look more like snakes than fish. But unlike snakes – and all bony fish apart from catfish – eels are entirely scaleless.

◆ More than 500 species of eel exist around the world in habitats ranging from marshes to coral reefs and the deep sea. All eels are predators, mostly of fish.

◆ Many marine eels are quite sedentary: garden eels spend most of their lives with their tails in the sand; moray eels ambush prey from crevices among rocks or coral; and conger eels spend the daylight hours holed up in lairs, emerging at night to hunt.

WEIRD AND WONDERFUL ❻

Anglerfish catch prey in the blink of an eye. Once they have drawn fish into range with their lure (see page 53) they snap them up in six thousandths of a second – one of the fastest movements in the entire animal kingdom.

★ 364

Seahorses and relatives

Seahorses look so unlike other fish many people do not realise that they are fish at all. They live in coastal waters, holding onto seaweed with their prehensile tails. Like their relatives, **pipefish** and **seadragons** (pictured), seahorses feed by sucking in invertebrates through their tubular mouths. The female lays her eggs in a brood pouch on the front of the male's body, and he subsequently 'gives birth' to the young. Seahorses are related to sticklebacks, which have similar bony armour beneath their skin.

IN DISGUISE The leafy seadragon (*Phycodurus eques*) mimics the seaweed it inhabits, drifting back and forth.

Tie-breaker ❼

Q: Which fish was thought to have been extinct for millions of years until one was caught in 1938?
A: The coelacanth (*Latimeria chalumnae*). This species is the sole survivor of the order Coelacanthiformes, a group with direct links to the first land-living vertebrates.

Amphibians

Core facts   ❶

◆ Amphibian is the common term for any member of the **vertebrate** class Amphibia.
◆ Most amphibians **lay eggs** that must remain damp to develop.
◆ Amphibians have soft, **thin skin** that is often moist or slimy.

◆ Most adult amphibians are **air-breathing** but can also absorb oxygen from water.
◆ Most adult amphibians have **four legs**. Their feet are usually either webbed for swimming or have toes with sticky pads for climbing.
◆ All adult amphibians are **active hunters**.

Types of amphibian   ❷

There are three orders in the class Amphibia:
◆ **Anura** includes all frogs and toads, which are tailless as adults and have much longer hind limbs than front.
◆ **Urodela** includes all salamanders and newts, which have four limbs of similar length and tails as adults.
◆ **Apoda** means 'without feet'. This order contains the caecilians – legless amphibians that resemble earthworms and come from the tropics.

Amphibian breathing   ❸

On the evolutionary scale amphibians lie in between fish and reptiles, and when it comes to obtaining oxygen they display characteristics of both. In their juvenile state most amphibians live in water and breathe through **gills** like fish. They lose these as they become adults and develop **lungs**, enabling them to breathe on land. Most amphibians can also breathe through their **skin**. Frogs, newts, salamanders and caecilians all have porous skin with meshes of blood capillaries near the surface to absorb oxygen.

RIVER DWELLER A salamander from North America, the hellbender (*Cryptobranchus alleganiensis*) grows to 75 cm (2$^{1}/_{2}$ ft) long. It hardly ever leaves the water and breathes entirely through its skin.

Tie-breaker   ❹

Q: Which island nation is home to the world's second largest amphibian?
A: Japan. The Japanese giant salamander (*Andrias japonicus*) is almost as massive as its Chinese cousin, weighing 40 kg (88 lb) and reaching 1.5 m (5 ft) long. Both giant salamanders eat frogs, crabs and fish.

Food and feeding   ❻

◆ All amphibians are **carnivorous** as adults, but most hunt prey far smaller than themselves. Among the exceptions is the goliath frog which hunts other vertebrates. The Amazonian horned frog (*Ceratophrys cornuta*) has such an enormous mouth that it can swallow prey almost as large as itself.
◆ Some amphibian tadpoles are **vegetarians**. Those of Europe's common frog (*Rana temporaria*) spend their first few weeks grazing water plants before moving on to meat.

Amphibian facts and figures   ❺

Frogs and toads

Longest (with legs extended)	Heaviest	Shortest (with legs extended)
American bullfrog *Rana catesbeiana* 91.5 cm (36 in)	Goliath frog *Conraua goliath* 3.65 kg (8 lb 1 oz)	Cuban frog *Sminthillus limbatus* 2.9 cm (1$^{1}/_{8}$ in)

Newts and salamanders

Longest	Heaviest	Shortest
Chinese giant salamander *Andrias davidianus* 1.8 m (5 ft 11 in)	Chinese giant salamander *Andrias davidianus* 65 kg (143 lb)	Mexican lungless salamander *Bolitoglossa mexicana* 2.5 cm (1 in)

Metamorphosis ❼

Amphibians have distinct juvenile and adult forms. Observing the metamorphosis from one to the other is almost like seeing evolution speeded up. Amphibians start life as free-swimming larvae, or tadpoles, that breathe with gills. As they grow older they lose their gills and develop lungs. **Frogs and toads**, which hatch legless and with tails, start to grow hindlegs after a few weeks, then they develop front legs and lose their tails. **Newts** hatch looking more like miniature adults but they too have gills that they lose as they grow older. Most **salamanders and caecilians** lay their eggs out of water and the young undergo metamorphosis before they hatch. A few caecilians and salamanders give birth to live young.

⭐ 154

One giant leap

The greatest jump by a frog was achieved by one of the smallest species. In 1975 at the Jumping Frog Jubilee in Calaveras County, California, a South African sharp-nosed frog (*Ptychadena oxyrhynchus*) called Ex Lax leapt 5.35 m (17 ft 6 in). These frogs grow to 6.5 cm (2½ in) so Ex Lax jumped over 80 times its bodylength.

Keep off – I'm deadly! ❽

Tropical America's **arrow poison frogs** produce some of the most potent nerve toxins in the animal kingdom. The deadliest of all is the golden arrow poison frog (*Phyllobates terribilis*). Although just 3.5 cm (1½ in) long, a single adult carries enough poison to kill almost 1000 people. These frogs advertise their danger through bright colours and bold patterns. There are about 60 species in all.

TRIBAL FAVOURITE *Dendrobates pumilio* has been used for centuries by Central American Indians.

GOOD FATHER Male *Dendrobates azureus* guard their mate's eggs until they hatch, then carry the young to water.

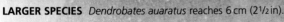
LARGER SPECIES *Dendrobates auaratus* reaches 6 cm (2½ in).

ONE OF A PAIR Most *Dendrobates leucomelas* are black with orange markings (above) but some individuals have blue stripes.

Birds 1

Core facts ❶

◆ Birds make up the second largest class of vertebrates, Aves. There are about **9000 species**.
◆ Birds are the only animals with feathers. They have two legs and a single pair of wings.
◆ Birds' jaws are **toothless** and covered by a layer of horn that forms a beak.
◆ Their **bones** are delicate and have air-filled cavities to save weight and make flight possible.
◆ Birds have a four-chambered heart and are **warm-blooded**. Their body temperature, on average, is 3°C higher than that of mammals.
◆ Most birds can fly – almost all of those that cannot are highly adapted either for swimming or running.

Masters of the air ❷

Birds include both the **largest and fastest flying animals** on Earth. They also include the **most airborne**; the sooty tern (*Sterna fuscata*) is believed to remain aloft for at least three years between fledging and breeding, while the swift (Apus apus) even mates on the wing.

Bird flight is often energy efficient. Large species such as vultures and albatrosses can **soar** for great distances without flapping their wings; vultures circle upwards on rising columns of hot air (thermals), while albatrosses ride on updrafts that form over the crests of waves. At the other extreme are hummingbirds, whose wings may beat 90 times a second. They can **hover** (stay stationary in mid air) without wind assistance for up to 50 minutes, and are also able to **fly backwards** – something that no other bird can do.

Primary wing feathers

Secondary wing feathers

Tail feathers

TAKING WING The grey heron (*Ardea cinerea*) is Britain's tallest native bird, and has a wingspan of up to 1.7 m (5 ft 8 in). Like all herons, it feeds mostly on fish.

Tie-breaker ❸

Q: Which flightless birds use their sense of smell to find food?
A: Kiwis. Kiwis are among the strangest of all birds. Nocturnal ground-dwellers, they have tiny wings, no tail and hair-like feathers. Kiwis use their sense of smell to locate the invertebrates that they feed on. They can even sniff out earthworms under the ground as they probe the soil with their long, thin bills.

TINY FLIER Cuba's bee hummingbird (*Mellisuga helenae*, pictured life-sized) is the world's smallest bird.

Bird facts and figures ❹

Greatest wingspan	Tallest	Heaviest	Heaviest flying	Fastest flying
Wandering albatross	Ostrich	Ostrich	Kori bustard	Peregrine falcon
Diomedea exulans	*Struthio camelus*	*Struthio camelus*	*Ardeotis kori*	*Falco peregrinus*
3.6 m (11 ft 10 in)	2.75 m (9 ft)	160 kg (350 lb)	19 kg (42 lb)	350 km/h (220 mph)

Eggs ❺

Some birds lay more eggs than others; the **largest clutch** ever recorded was of 28 eggs laid by a bobwhite quail (*Colinus virginiatus*). The **fastest incubator** of its eggs is the red-billed quelea (*Quelea quelea*) – its chicks hatch out after just 10 days.

The **largest eggs** are those laid by the ostrich; the biggest ever measured weighed 2.3 kg (5.1 lb). The record for the **smallest bird's egg** belongs to one of the smallest birds – the vervain hummingbird (*Mellisuga minima*) from Jamaica.

Vervain hummingbird egg (actual size)

9 mm (1/3 in)

Bird classification ❻

Birds are classified into 27 different orders. The largest, Passeriformes, contains more than half of all the species.

Order	Common name	Number of species
Anseriformes	Ducks, geese and swans	148
Apodiformes	Swifts and hummingbirds	388
Apterygiformes	Kiwis	3
Caprimulgiformes	Frogmouths and nightjars	94
Casuariiformes	Emus and cassowaries	4
Charadriiformes	Auks, waders, gulls and skuas	294
Ciconiiformes	Herons, storks and flamingoes	120
Coliiformes	Colies or mousebirds	6
Columbiformes	Pigeons and sandgrouse	305
Coraciiformes	Kingfishers and hornbills	190
Cuculiformes	Cuckoos and turacos	147
Falconiformes	Birds of prey	271
Galliformes	Game birds and hoatzin	251
Gaviiformes	Divers	4
Gruiformes	Cranes, rails and bustards	197
Passeriformes	Passerines or perching birds. Range in size from wrens to crows.	About 5400
Pelecaniformes	Pelicans and gannets	59
Piciformes	Woodpeckers, barbets and toucans	400
Podicipediformes	Grebes	21
Procellariiformes	Albatrosses, petrels and fulmars	91
Psittaciformes	Parrots	315
Rheiformes	Rheas	2
Sphenisciformes	Penguins	18
Strigiformes	Owls	130
Struthioniformes	Ostrich	1
Tinamiformes	Tinamous	50
Trogoniformes	Trogons, include the quetzal (*Pharomachrus mocinno*)	35

Ostrich egg (actual size)

19 cm (7 1/2 in)

WEIRD AND WONDERFUL ❼

Kiwis lay larger eggs in proportion to body size than any other birds. A 1.7 kg (3 3/4 lb) brown kiwi (*Apteryx australis*) may lay two eggs in as many days, each weighing 450 g (1 lb) – 26 per cent of its own body-weight.

★ 615

Breathing

Birds' breathing is much more efficient than our own. Air passes right through their relatively rigid lungs into sacs scattered throughout the body, including the bones. Upon breathing out, the air flows back through the lungs a second time, enabling more oxygen to be extracted from it.

Birds 2

Perching birds ①

The majority of the world's birds are **passerines**, or perching birds. Most are small and all have grasping feet with three toes that point forwards and one that points backwards. Passerine chicks hatch out blind, naked and helpless and are usually cared for by both parents until they are able to fend for themselves.

The perching bird order, Passeriformes, contains 56 families, including swallows, tits, thrushes, larks, wagtails, finches, starlings and crows. All songbirds are perching birds.

FAMILIAR FACE
The house sparrow (*Passer domesticus*) occurs around the world.

Tie-breaker

Q: Which black and white bird has a reputation for stealing? ②
A: The magpie. The magpie (*Pica pica*) occurs across Eurasia and in western North America. Like the raven, nutcrackers, choughs and jays, it is a member of the crow family Corvidae.

Dead as a dodo ③

Flightless birds are rare in evolution and they have become even less common since people spread around the globe. The most famous extinct flightless bird is the dodo (*Raphus cucullatus*). Like the **kakapo** (*Strigops habroptilus*), a giant parrot from New Zealand that still survives in small numbers, the dodo lost the ability to fly by evolving on an island (Mauritius) with no large land-based predators. The arrival of people and the rats they inadvertently introduced saw it disappear within decades. The last dodo died in 1662.

Several other flightless birds became extinct in recent centuries. The 11 species of **moa**, giant relatives of the emu, were hunted to extinction by the Maoris in the 1300s. And Madagascar's **elephant bird** (*Aepyornis maximus*) disappeared in the 17th century.

GONE FOR EVER The great auk (*Pinguinus impennis*) was the northern equivalent of the penguin.

The hood calms the bird and is removed once the handler is ready to release it.

★ **530**

Falconry

The art of hunting with birds of prey dates back to at least 2000 BC. It is still practised in some places today; the Kazakh people of Mongolia, for instance, use golden eagles (*Aquila chrysaetos*) to hunt foxes and other fur-bearing animals.

Like many sports, falconry has developed its own terminology. Male birds often have their own particular name; male falcons are called tiercels, while a male sparrowhawk (*Falco sparverius*) is known as a musket, for example.

BIRD IN THE HAND A gyrfalcon (*Falco rusticolus*) perches on a falconer's gauntlet. Thongs known as jesses around the bird's ankles attach it to a leash, which runs through a metal ring on the gauntlet.

Birds of prey ❹

Birds of prey feed on other animals and **all are diurnal** (active by day). Eagles, buzzards, harriers, kites, hawks and falcons are skilled hunters, capturing prey with feet armed with sharp, curved talons. Once the quarry is dead it is torn apart using a hooked beak.

All birds of prey have very keen eyesight and one group, the vultures, has a well-developed sense of smell. Vultures are birds of prey that scavenge for a living. Most have bald heads enabling them to rummage inside carcasses without getting feathers matted. The **largest** bird of prey, the Andean condor (*Vultur gryphus*), is a vulture. The title of **smallest** bird of prey is shared by the black-legged falconet (*Microhierax fringillarius*) and the white-fronted falconet (*M. latifrons*), both from Southeast Asia: neither is any bigger than a starling.

DIVE BOMBER
The osprey (*Pandion haliaetus*) lives entirely on fish which it catches by plunging into water feet first. Neither falcon nor eagle, it has been given its own family by scientists, Pandionidae. Here, an adult brings a fish back to the nest for its chicks.

WEIRD AND WONDERFUL ❺

The **highest flying bird** ever recorded was a Ruppell's griffon vulture (*Gyps ruppellii*). It was identified from feathers after hitting the engine of a commercial aircraft 11 277 m (37 000 ft) over the Ivory Coast.

Owls ❻

◆ Owls are **meat-eaters** but are not classified as birds of prey. Most **hunt at night** and all have huge, forward-facing eyes.
◆ Owls can turn their heads through 360°.
◆ All owls have exceptional hearing and can pinpoint prey by sound alone.
◆ The **most widespread** species is the barn owl (*Tyto alba*), which has an almost global distribution. The **largest** is Europe's great eagle owl (*Bubo bubo*); and the **smallest** the elf owl (*Micrathene whitneyi*) from North America.

ARCTIC HUNTER The snowy owl (*Nyctea scandiaca*) is the world's most northerly owl. It feeds on birds and small mammals. Unlike many other owl species, it hunts in daylight.

Flags flying ❼

Fourteen countries have birds on their national flags, six of them opting for eagles.

Country	Bird
Albania	Double-headed eagle
Dominica	Imperial Amazon parrot (Sisserou)
Ecuador	Andean condor
Egypt	Eagle
Fiji	Dove
Guatemala	Quetzal
Kazakhstan	Eagle
Kiribati	Frigatebird
Mexico	Eagle (and rattlesnake)
Moldova	Eagle
Papua New Guinea	Raggiana bird of paradise
Uganda	Grey crowned crane
Zambia	Eagle
Zimbabwe	Great Zimbabwe bird (mythical)

Albania

Dominica

Kiribati

Papua New Guinea

Birds 3

Wildfowl ①

Wildfowl include waterfowl and game birds. Game birds are poor fliers, spending most of their time on the ground.

Family	Examples
Anatidae Ducks, geese and swans (145 species)	Mallard duck (*Anas platyrhynchos*) Canada goose (*Branta canadensis*) Mute swan (*Cygnus olor*)
Meleagrididae Turkeys (2 species)	Wild turkey (*Meleagris gallopavo*) Ocellated turkey (*Agriocharis ocellata*)
Numididae Guineafowl (10 species)	Helmeted guineafowl (*Numidia meleagris*) Vulturine guineafowl (*Acryllium vulturinum*)
Phasianidae Fowl (165 species)	Ringed pheasant (*Phasianus colchicus*) Red junglefowl (*Gallus gallus*)
Tetraonidae Grouse (18 species)	Black grouse (*Lyrurus tetrix*) Capercaillie (*Tetrao urogallus*)

GAME BIRD The red grouse (*Lagopus lagopus*).

Birds on books ③

Publisher/packager	Founded
Eagle Wing Books	1986
Falcon Publishing	1979
Flamingo (imprint of HarperCollins)	1981
Kingfisher	1973
Pelican Publishing	1926
Penguin	1935
Prion Books	1979
Puffin (children's imprint of Penguin)	1939
Toucan Books	1985
Turnstone Press	1975

WEIRD AND WONDERFUL ②

The **eiderdown** that fills fine quilts and pillows comes from the nests of eider ducks (*Somateria mollissima*). The wild ducks pluck the feathers from their breasts for insulation. The down is collected after the ducklings have flown.

★ 740

Sun seekers

Southern Africa's **jackass penguins** (*Spheniscus demersus*) come ashore at beach resorts and on the edge of the Namib desert, among other places. Named for their braying call, they nest on offshore islands and the mainland.

A resident of the Galapagos islands on the Equator, the **Galapagos penguin** (*Spheniscus mendiculus*) is the most northerly penguin species.

BACK TO BASE
A Cape gannet
(*Morus capensis*)
returns to its
breeding colony
from a fishing
trip. This species
dives from the air
to capture prey.

Ocean wanderers

❹

More than 200 bird species spend most of their lives over
the sea. Gannets, petrels, boobies, shearwaters and auks
all scan the waves in search of fish and other creatures.
When they find prey some birds, such as terns, dive at it
from the air. Others, such as gulls, land and pick it from
or near the surface. Still others, such as cormorants,
alight on the water then dive after their prey.

Birds' beaks

❺

Birds' beaks are **modified jaws** covered with a layer of horn.
The first birds had teeth but these were lost through
evolution to save weight and reduce
energy expenditure in flight.
   Beaks come in many shapes
and sizes, each reflecting
its owner's diet.

Those of
generalist feeders,
such as crows, have a
relatively simple, multipurpose
design, while those of waders, such as
the curlew (*Numenicus arquata*, below left)
are long and thin for probing through mud.
The **longest beak** of any bird belongs to the Australian
pelican (*Pelicanus conspicillatus*, below). It measures up to
47 cm (18 in) and has a capacity, including the pouch,
of three times that of the bird's stomach.

FILTER FEEDER Beaks
are shaped to help birds
feed. Greater flamingos
(*Phoenicopterus ruber*,
right) use theirs as sieves
to filter tiny organisms
from the water.

Flightless seabirds

❻

Some seabirds have become so at home
in water that they have lost the ability
to fly. **Penguins**, which share a
common ancestor with albatrosses,
became flightless at least 30 million
years ago. Other seabirds have lost the

power of flight more recently. The
Galapagos flightless cormorant
(*Nannopterum harrisi*) is the only
member of its order (Pelecaniformes)
unable to fly. It retains a full set of flight
feathers of reduced size and strength.

QUESTION NUMBER

The numbers or star following the answers refer to information boxes on the right.

ANSWERS

8	Canines ❸
88	Mammal ❶ ❻
141	Snake – all of the others are mammals
163	Omnivore ❸
216	False – amphibians, for example, have neither
342	Teeth ❸
★ 401	False (they are both mammals) ★
404	True ❹
582	None ❶
673	Marsupials are mammals ❷
820	Bats ❶
867	Dogs (carnivores) ❷
925	Scales (all of the rest are features of mammals) ❶
984	True ❹

Mammals

Core facts ❶

◆ Mammals make up the vertebrate class **Mammalia**, which contains the largest and most familiar animals, including ourselves. There are more than **4000 species**.
◆ They are **warm-blooded** and **breathe air**.
◆ They have mammary glands and feed their young on **milk**.
◆ Most mammals live on land, but three orders – the cetaceans, pinnipeds and sea cows – spend their lives in water.
◆ Bats (order Chiroptera) are the only flying vertebrates apart from birds.
◆ All mammals have **hair** except for those, such as dolphins, which have lost it at some point during their evolution. Most mammals have more than one type of tooth.

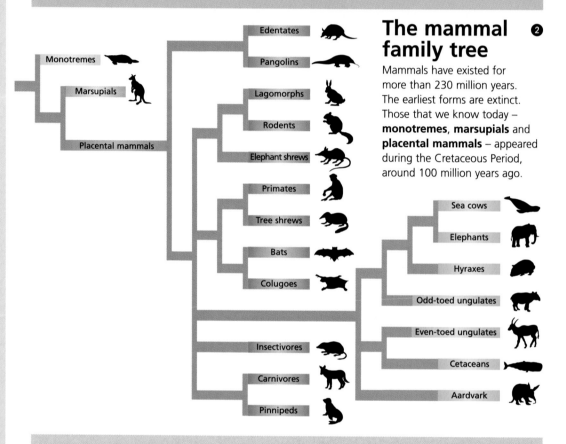

The mammal family tree ❷

Mammals have existed for more than 230 million years. The earliest forms are extinct. Those that we know today – **monotremes**, **marsupials** and **placental mammals** – appeared during the Cretaceous Period, around 100 million years ago.

Mammal teeth

Mammals are the only animals to have more than one type of teeth in their mouths. Unlike fish, amphibians and reptiles, which have many virtually identical teeth, mammals have fixed ❸ numbers of three different types: **incisors**, **canines** and **molars**. Each type fulfils a different function and are more developed in some animals than others, depending on eating habits.

CARNIVORE TEETH Carnivores have long, curved canines for stabbing flesh and holding on to prey. Their 'molars' (carnassials) are sharp-edged for cutting.

HERBIVORE TEETH Herbivores eat only plant matter, which is harder to digest than meat. Grinding molars break the plant matter down before swallowing.

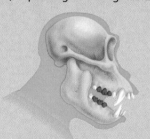

OMNIVORE TEETH Omnivores, such as chimpanzees, eat a wide range of food and have teeth that are less specialised than those of carnivores or herbivores.

Hair ④

Like birds, mammals are **endothermic** (warm-blooded), which means they can control their body temperatures without help from their surroundings. Hair helps them do this by trapping an insulating layer of still air against their bodies. This keeps heat in and so cuts down the amount of food mammals need to eat (food is the 'fuel' that animals break down to produce energy, including heat).

FUR COATS Long, thick hair enables musk-oxen (*Ovibos moschatus*) to survive low temperatures.

WEIRD AND WONDERFUL ⑤

Humans are the only truly **bipedal** mammals. Several other species can move on their hind legs but none do so exclusively. The closest contenders, kangaroos and wallabies, use their forelimbs when not travelling

Milk ⑥

All mammals feed their young on milk, a nutrient-rich growth food which supplies all of a young animal's needs. As well as providing sustenance, milk enables a mother to pass on any antibodies to disease that she might have acquired and so immunise her young.

Mammals have between one and 31 offspring at a time and different species have different numbers of teats, ranging from two in creatures such as primates to 29 in the mammal with the most – Madagascar's common tenrec (*Tenrec ecaudatus*), which also holds the record for the largest litter.

CLOSE FAMILY
Mammals have strong bonds with their young. Grizzly bear cubs like these stay with their mother for up to four years.

⭐ 401

Built to swim

Dolphins and **porpoises** look like fish but are no more related to them than we are. Their similar appearance is an example of convergent evolution – they have evolved the best shape for moving through water, just as fish did millions of years earlier.

Mammal facts and figures ⑦

Largest	Largest on land	Smallest	Smallest on land
Blue whale	African elephant	Kitti's hog-nosed bat	Etruscan shrew
Balaenoptera musculus	*Loxodonta africana*	*Craseonycteris thonglongyai*	*Suncus etruscus*
200 tonnes	12 tonnes	1.7–2 g (0.6–0.7 oz)	1.5–2.5 g (0.5–0.9 oz)

Sloths and anteaters

Core facts ❶

◆ South America's anteaters, armadillos and sloths belong to the order **Edentata**. Edentata means toothless, although it is only the anteaters (family Myrmecophagidae) that do not have teeth. Africa and Asia have their own versions of anteaters; the aardvark and pangolins.

◆ **Sloths** are creatures of tropical rain forest.

There are five species in two genera.

◆ **Armadillos** live in a variety of lowland habitats and feed mainly on invertebrates.

◆ The **aardvark** is the sole member of the order Tubulidentata. It has only molar teeth.

◆ **Pangolins** occur in Africa, India and Southeast Asia. There are seven species.

NO STRAIN Three-toed sloths are lighter than their two-toed cousins.

Sloths ❷

◆ Sloths are the **slowest mammals** on Earth. The pale-throated three-toed sloth (*Bradypus tridactylus*) is the slowest of all with a top speed of just 4.6 m/min (15 ft/min).

◆ Sloths spend most of their lives in the trees, descending just once every few days to defecate. The reason for their sluggishness is partly their poor diet. Sloths feed only on leaves, many of which are too poisonous for other animals to digest.

Pangolins ❸

Pangolins share features with anteaters and armadillos, but are not related to either. These **tree-climbing** mammals have a long, sticky tongue to feed on ants and termites. They also have body armour, which unlike that of armadillos is made of overlapping scales formed from horn. The scales are periodically replaced.

HARD CASE With its tail wrapped around itself, a pangolin presents a tough challenge to any predator.

 127

Africa's ground hog

With its long snout, rabbit-like ears and robust body, the **aardvark** is one of the strangest of all African mammals. Secretive and nocturnal, it is rarely seen, despite the fact that it may reach almost 2 m (6 ft 6 in) and weigh more than a man.

NIGHT OUTING The aardvark (*Orycteropus afer*) lives in a burrow during the day.

Anteaters ❹

Armed with fearsome claws and a 61 cm (24 in) long tongue, the **giant anteater** (*Myrmecophaga tridactyla*) tears open termite mounds and licks up their inhabitants. It has a voracious appetite and may eat up to 30 000 termites a day.

The giant anteater lives on Argentina's pampas and is the largest of three species. The other two, the **tamandua** (*Tamandua mexicana*) and **pygmy anteater** (*Cyclopes didactylus*) are both tree-climbing forest-dwellers with prehensile tails. As its name suggests, the pygmy anteater is the smallest species; at about 15 cm (6 in) long it is small enough to sit in the palm of a man's hand.

Armadillos ❺

◆ The word armadillo comes from the Spanish for armoured, *armado*.
◆ There are 20 species, ranging in size from the 85 g (3 oz) **pink fairy armadillo** (*Chlamyphorus truncatus*) to the 50 kg (110 lb) **giant armadillo** (*Priodontes maximus*).
◆ All live in South or Central America apart from the **nine-banded armadillo** (*Dasypus novemcinctus*), which ranges as far north as the USA.

Tie-breaker ❻

Q: Which tree-living mammals spend most of their lives upside-down?
A: Sloths. Sloths only right themselves to climb up or down the trunks of trees, and when they are on the ground. They eat, sleep, move, mate and even give birth hanging from their hooked claws.

ON THE MOVE A giant anteater crosses a river. This species covers itself with its tail when sleeping.

Rodents and rabbits

Core facts ❶

◆ Rabbits and rodents belong to two separate orders. **Rabbits** are part of the order **Lagomorpha** along with hares and pikas. **Rodents** comprise the order **Rodentia**, which is split into three suborders, each defined by bodyform. All rabbits and rodents are herbivores.
◆ The suborder Myomorpha contains all of the **mouse-like** rodents – more than a quarter of all mammals, with 1082 species recognised to date. Mouse-like rodents are defined by their cheek teeth, which occur in rows of three. Nearly all are small, nocturnal, land-living seed-eaters.
◆ **Squirrel-like** rodents have rows of four cheek teeth (molars) and make up the suborder Sciuromorpha. They include almost all tree-living rodents, although many are terrestrial and some, such as beavers, live in water.
◆ The third suborder, Cavimorpha, contains the **cavy-like** rodents. Most have rounded snouts and a few dig burrows. Cavimorphs include the largest rodents – porcupines and the capybara.
◆ **Rabbits** and **hares** make up the family Leporidae. They have long ears, long hind limbs and short, upturned tails. There are 44 species. Pikas comprise the family Ochotonidae. They have short ears and no tail. There are 14 species.

The world's most successful mammals ❷

Almost half of the world's species of mammal are rodents. Adaptable and tough, they have colonised almost every habitat on land. The reason for their success is twofold: firstly, they can eat just about anything, and secondly they breed at a phenomenal rate. The female **Norway lemming** (*Lemmus lemmus*) can conceive at just 14 days old. And the **house mouse** (*Mus musculus*) can produce 14 litters of six babies each year.

Rodents come in a huge variety of shapes and sizes. They include rats, mice, squirrels, porcupines and beavers to name but a few. Some rodents, such as flying squirrels, can glide through the air, while others such as kangaroo rats and the springhare (*Pedetes capensis*) jump on their hind legs.

AQUATIC GIANT South America's capybara (*Hydrochoerus hydrochaeris*) is the world's largest rodent. Adult males can measure 1.4 m (4¹/₂ ft) long.

Rodents and people ❸

Over the centuries rodents have caused more suffering to humans than any other group of mammals. As carriers of typhus, the fleas that cause black death, and other diseases, rats and mice have accounted for more deaths than all the wars in history. The **brown rat** (*Rattus norvegicus*) and **house mouse** are thought to have originated in Asia. They can now be found on every continent, including Antarctica.

STOCKING UP A North American pika (*Ochotona princeps*) carries leaves to its winter store.

Pikas

58

Pikas are the smallest lagomorphs. Mountain-dwelling species breed in summer and spend winter in their burrows. They spend the autumn collecting vegetation which keeps them going in harsher times.

Fictional favourites

4

Talking animals have long been a staple of children's fiction, and rabbits and rodents are particularly popular characters.

Author	Book (year published)	Character	Species
Lewis Carroll	*Alice's Adventures in Wonderland* (1865)	**Dormouse**	Dormouse *Muscardinus avellanarius*
		March Hare	Brown hare *Lepus europaeus*
		White Rabbit	Rabbit *Oryctolagus cuniculus*
Beatrix Potter	*The Tale of Squirrel Nutkin* (1903)	**Squirrel Nutkin**	Red squirrel *Sciurus vulgaris*
Joel C. Harris	*Uncle Remus and Brer Rabbit* (1880)	**Brer Rabbit**	Cottontail *Sylvilagus floridanus*
E.B. White	*Charlotte's Web* (1974)	**Templeton**	Brown rat *Rattus norvegicus*
Kenneth Grahame	*The Wind in the Willows* (1908)	**Ratty**	Water vole *Arvicola terrestris*

TEA FOR THREE Lewis Carroll's Alice sits down with the March Hare and dormouse at the Mad Hatter's tea party.

Rabbits and hares

5

◆ Rabbits and hares are all ground-dwelling herbivores. They occur all over the world living in habitats ranging from rain forest to desert.

◆ Rabbits and hares are built for speed. Some of the larger hares, such as the **Alaskan hare** (*Lepus othus*), can reach 80 km/h (50 mph).

◆ A few rabbits and hares are endangered. The **Amami rabbit** (*Pentalagus furnessi*), for example, is found only on two small islands off Japan and the entire world population is thought to number no more than 5000. The **volcano rabbit** (*Romerolagus diazi*) is even rarer. It lives on the volcanic slopes outside Mexico City.

17 cm (6³/4 in)

RADIATORS The antelope jackrabbit (*Lepus alleni*) has the longest ears of any lagomorph. It lives in the deserts of north-western Mexico and the southern USA.

Tie-breaker

6

Q: Which group of mammals gets its name from the Greek verb 'to gnaw'?
A: Rodents (*from rodere*). Rodents' teeth continue to grow throughout life and they must gnaw to wear them down.

The numbers or star following the answers refer to information boxes on the right.

QUESTION NUMBER

ANSWERS

33	A roar ❷
79	The lion ❷ ❻
175	Lion ❸
223	Tiger – Tiger Woods
232	The lion ❷
246	India (specifically the Gir Forest) ❷
289	Civet ❼
292	Ford ❹
293	The Beetle ❹
298	Jaguar ❹
454	Ferrari ❹
457	A lion ❹
458	A tiger ❷
587	Lions – from the Portuguese *serra lyoa*
745	The Dodge Viper ❹
783	True ❷
810	Lynx ❷
877	Wild cat (*Felis sylvestris*) ❷
891	Tiger ❷
913	Golden cat – from Southeast Asia
951	*Felis sylvestris* – ancestor of the domestic cat
★ 975	A lion and a tiger ★

Carnivores 1

Core facts ❶

◆ The word **carnivore** is drawn from the Latin carnivorous, 'meat-devouring'. In everyday language it is used as a general term for any animal that eats meat, but to biologists it refers only to members of the order Carnivora.

◆ There are **seven families** of carnivore split into two suborders; the **cat-like** carnivores (Aeluroidea) and the **dog-like** carnivores (Arctoidea, overleaf).

◆ **Cats** have five toes on their front feet and four on the rear. They are lightly built meat-eaters that stalk or ambush their prey.

◆ **Hyenas** have longer front than hind limbs which gives them an ungainly appearance.

◆ **Viverrids**, which include all civets, genets and mongooses, are closest in appearance to the ancestral carnivores. They have long bodies, short legs and long, generally bushy, tails.

Cats ❷

The cat family **Felidae** contains 37 species. All except the **cheetah** (*Acinonyx jubatus*) can fully retract their claws.

There are seven species of big cat: the **lion** (*Panthera leo*), **tiger** (*Panthera tigris*), **jaguar** (*Panthera onca*), **leopard** (*Panthera pardus*), **snow leopard** (*Panthera uncia*), **cheetah** (*Acinonyx jubatus*) and **clouded leopard** (*Neofelis nebulosa*). Lions live in Africa and the **Gir Forest** of Gujurat, India. The tiger is the largest of the big cats and the leopard, which ranges from Africa to central and southern Asia, is the most widespread.

There are 30 species of small cat, including the puma, ocelot, lynx and wild cat. The puma (*Felis concolor*) is the most adaptable, occurring from Canada to Argentina. Like all of the smaller cats, it can purr but not roar.

SPANISH RARITY The Iberian lynx (*Lynx pardinus*) is the world's rarest cat. Lynxes can be identified by their tufted ears and short tails.

WEIRD AND WONDERFUL ❸

The word for lion in Malay, Thai and many other south Asian languages is singa (singha) or singh. All Sikhs have the surname **Singh**, meaning lion, and Singapore translates literally as The Lion City.

Creatures on cars ❹

Several motor vehicle manufacturers use cats or other animals as logos.

Company	Creature
Alfa Romeo	Snake
Bobcat	Bobcat
Dodge	Ram
Ferrari	Prancing horse
Jaguar	Jaguar
Lambourghini	Bull
Peugeot	Lion
Porsche	Horse
Saab	Griffin's head
Vauxhall	Griffin

Zoo hybrids

Lions and tigers are so closely related that they may interbreed. The offspring are known as **ligers** if the father was a lion or **tigons** if the father was a tiger. All male ligers and tigons are infertile, although females can conceive. Interbreeding has also been recorded in Japanese and Italian zoos between lions and **leopards**. The young are known as leopons.

MIXED GENES A male tigon in a Polish zoo. Lions and tigers are so similar anatomically that even experts are unable to tell their skeletons apart.

Hyenas ❺

There are four species of hyena. The **spotted**, or **laughing**, **hyena** (*Crocuta crocuta*) is the only group-living species (see page 59). It eats meat, as do the **brown hyena** (*Hyaena brunnea*) and **striped hyena** (*Hyaena hyaena*). The **aardwolf** (*Proteles cristatus*), lives entirely on termites and ants. Its jaws are relatively weak, whereas those of the other species can crush bone. Hyenas live only in Africa apart from the striped hyena, which ranges from north Africa through the Middle East to India.

Civets and their relatives ❼

◆ The family Viverridae is the largest in the order Carnivora, with around 75 species, all found in Africa and Eurasia.
◆ The species range in size from Africa's smallest predator, the 320 g (11¼ oz) **dwarf mongoose** (*Helogale parvula*), to the **African civet** (*Civettictis civetta*) which reaches 20 kg (44 lb).
◆ Nearly all viverrids have scent glands and civets are still hunted for their musk, which is used in perfume.
◆ Genets and civets are nocturnal; mongooses are active by day.

CAT-LIKE POSE
The common genet (*Genetta genetta*) occurs from Africa to southwestern Europe.

Big cats under threat ❻

Lions and tigers once divided Africa and Eurasia between them, but today their ranges are seriously reduced. The Barbary lion (*Panthera leo leo*), which once roamed from Morocco to Egypt, is now extinct in the wild, as is the Cape lion (*P. l. melanochaitus*). Three subspecies of tiger, the Balinese (*Panthera tigris balica*), Javan (*P. t. sondaica*) and Caspian (*P. t. virgata*), have been wiped out entirely.

Distribution of lions

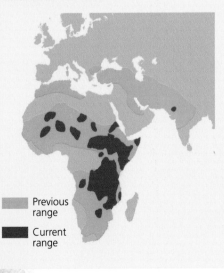

Previous range

Current range

Distribution of tigers

Previous range

Current range

Carnivores 2

Dogs ❶

The dog family, **Canidae**, contains 37 species. They range in size from the 1.3 kg (2 lb) **Blandford's fox** (*Vulpes cana*) to the **grey wolf** (*Canis lupus*), which may weigh 103 kg (227 lb).

Long-legged carnivores with bushy tails, dogs are mostly good runners that move on the tips of their toes. Many of the larger species, such as southern Asia's **dhole** (*Cuon alpinus*), are pack-living animals that hunt by chasing prey over long distances. Most **coyotes**, **jackals** and **foxes**, however, are solitary and hunt creatures much smaller than themselves.

The most widespread dog today is the **red fox** (*Vulpes vulpes*). Its natural range encompasses much of North America, Eurasia and northern Africa. It has also been introduced to Australia.

DISAPPEARING ACT The grey wolf was once the world's most widespread carnivore. Now virtually exterminated from Europe and the USA, it thrives only where people are absent.

Tie-breaker ❷

Q: By what name is the glutton (*Gulo gulo*) better known?
A: Wolverine. Found in taiga and tundra across the Northern Hemisphere, this powerfully built member of the weasel family is renowned for its strength as well as its appetite. It will challenge wolves and even bears for their kills.

Male and female ❸

Some carnivores have particular names for the two sexes.

Animal	Male	Female
Badgers, bears	Boar	Sow
Domestic cat	Tom	Queen
Dogs, otters	Dog	Bitch
Foxes	Dog	Vixen

COSY COAT The sea otter (*Enhydra lutra*) has the densest fur of any mammal. Found off the western coast of North America, it sleeps while afloat, often wrapped in kelp to prevent itself from drifting out to sea.

Life in the water ❹

◆ Otters belong to the family Mustelidae and are the only carnivores to specialise in hunting fish. There are 11 species.

◆ They occur in the rivers of every continent except for Australia and Antarctica.

◆ The largest is South America's **giant otter** (*Pteronura brasiliensis*) and the smallest the **Asian short-clawed otter** (*Aonyx cineria*) from southern India and Southeast Asia, which reaches a maximum length of 90 cm (3 ft).

WEIRD AND WONDERFUL ❺

The teddy bear was named after **Theodore Roosevelt**. In 1902 Roosevelt took a hunting trip in Mississippi, where he spared a very old bear from being shot. The story found its way into the newspapers and the teddy bear was born.

Bears ❻

Although classed as carnivores, all bears are omnivorous. The smallest of the seven species is the sun bear (*Helarctos malayanus*), reaching just 1.4 m (4 ft 7 in) long. The **brown bear** is the most widespread.

WAITING GAME The grizzly bear (*Ursus arctos horribilis*) from North America is one of five subspecies of brown bear. Others include the blue bear (*U. a. pruinosus*), Syrian bear (*U. a. syriacus*) and Himalayan brown bear (*U. a. isabellinus*).

Weasels, minks and martens ❼

The family Mustelidae includes weasels, stoats, martens, otters, badgers, skunks and minks. All have short legs and long, flexible bodies and most are small animals – the heaviest is the sea otter, which can weigh 45 kg (99 lb). Mustelids occur from the poles to the tropics. Many are fierce hunters, capable of killing prey much larger than themselves.

WINTER WARDROBE The stoat (*Mustela erminea*) is the only mustelid to turn white in winter.

★ 874

Bandit country

With its black-and-white bandit mask and thick ringed tail, the **raccoon** (*Procyon lotor*) is one of North America's most easily recognised animals. This adaptable carnivore has made itself at home in most of the continent's towns and cities, seemingly as happy to live on rubbish and road kills as its more natural diet of eggs and small animals. The raccoon is just one member of a large family of carnivores. Its cousins include the **ringtail** (*Bassariscus astutus*) and South America's **coati** (*Nasua nasua*).

Seals and sea lions

Core facts   ●

◆ Seals and sea lions are grouped into the order Pinnipeda, which means 'wing foot' in Latin. **Pinnipeds** are closely related to the land-based carnivores and are all flesh-eating mammals. There are three families.

◆ **True seals** belong to the family Phocidae. They have sleek hair and no external ear flaps.

◆ **Sea lions** belong to the family Otariidae. Also known as eared seals, they have external ear flaps and are covered with a thick coat of fur. Unlike true seals, sea lions can use their front flippers to raise their bodies up off the ground.

◆ The third family, Odobenidae, has just one member, the **walrus**, which has hairless skin.

Pinniped facts and figures   ❷

Longest	Shortest	Commonest	Rarest
Southern elephant seal	Galapagos fur seal	Crabeater seal	Mediterranean monk seal
Mirounga leonina	*Arctocephalus galapagoensis*	*Lobodon carcinophagus*	*Monachus monachus*
5 m (16 ft 6 in)	1.5 m (5 ft)	About 13 million	About 500

⭐ **323**

Trouble in paradise

Most pinnipeds are creatures of icy waters but **monk seals** are found only in subtropical seas. Their choice of habitat has led to a history of conflict with humans. Of the original three species, one, the Caribbean monk seal (*Monachus tropicalis*), has already been driven to extinction by fishermen and disturbance of its breeding beaches.

OUT OF ITS ELEMENT Antarctica has no native land mammals, so the leopard seal (*Hydrurga leptonyx*) is the closest thing the continent has to a polar bear. A predator of penguins, the seal usually hunts in the water but occasionally tries its luck out on the ice.

Breeding and birth ❸

All pinnipeds come ashore to breed. To minimise danger from predators on land, most gather in large numbers on secluded beaches. Breeding colonies of **northern fur seals** (*Callorhinus ursinus*) on the Alaskan islands of St George and St Paul have the greatest concentration of large mammals on Earth, with an estimated 900 000 animals.

Some seal species give birth alone. The **ringed seal** (*Pusa hispida*) avoids predators by pupping in a cave under the snow. Other species have different techniques for staying safe. The **hooded seal** has the shortest lactation period of any mammal, nursing its pup for just four days before leading it into the water.

CROWDED BEACH Hundreds of walruses (*Odobenus rosmarus*) fill a beach on the coast of the Bering Sea.

WEIRD AND WONDERFUL ❹
The male **hooded seal** (*Cystophora cristata*) threatens rivals by inflating its head. The seal either blows up its red nasal cavity lining, which comes out of one nostril, or it inflates the balloon-like black hood on the front of its face.

Built to swim ❺

◆ Pinnipeds evolved from carnivores about 15 million years ago. At first they resembled their land cousins closely, but as time passed they adapted ever more to life in the sea.
◆ Today's pinnipeds still show similarities to their ancestors, particularly in their skulls and teeth. Their bodies, however,

STREAMLINED GRACE The California sea lion (*Zalophus californianus*) ranges as far south as the Galapagos.

have altered immensely. **Sea lions** can still lift their bodies up with their hind limbs, but true seals are unable to do even that.
◆ Other adaptations to marine life are less visible. The capacity of blood to hold oxygen is greatly increased and seals can slow their metabolism right down when diving. The deepest diver, the **northern elephant seal** (*Mirounga angustirostris*), can hold its breath for well over an hour and has been recorded diving to more than 1500 m (5000 ft).

RELAXED LOOK A Weddell seal (*Leptonychotes weddelli*) takes a rare break on the Antarctic ice. A hunter of squid and bottom-living fish, the Weddell seal can dive to 550 m (1800 ft).

Hoofed mammals

Core facts

◆ Hoofed mammals (**ungulates**) all have a reduced number of functional toes, each of which is covered by a horny sheath.
◆ Hoofed mammals are divided into **two orders**, the Perissodactyla, or odd-toed hoofed mammals, and the Artiodactyla, or even-toed hoofed mammals. All are herbivores, apart from pigs and peccaries, which are omnivores.

◆ **Odd-toed** hoofed mammals include rhinoceroses and horses. There are 15 species.
◆ **Even-toed** hoofed mammals are split into three suborders: Suiformes, which contains the pigs, peccaries and hippos; Tylopoda, which includes the camels; and Ruminanta, which contains the ruminants – chevrotains, deer, cattle, antelopes, giraffes and the pronghorn.

Ungulate facts and figures ❷

Odd-toed

Tallest	Heaviest	Lightest
White rhinoceros	White rhinoceros	Mountain tapir
Ceratotherium simium	*Ceratotherium simium*	*Tapirus pinchaque*
1.85 m (6 ft) at shoulder	Up to 3.6 tonnes	225 kg (500 lb)

Even-toed

Tallest	Heaviest	Lightest
Giraffe	Common hippopotamus	Lesser mouse deer
Giraffa camelopardalis	*Hippopotamus amphibius*	*Tragulus javanicus*
6 m (20 ft)	Up to 4 tonnes	1.7–3 kg (3³/₄–6¹/₂ lb)

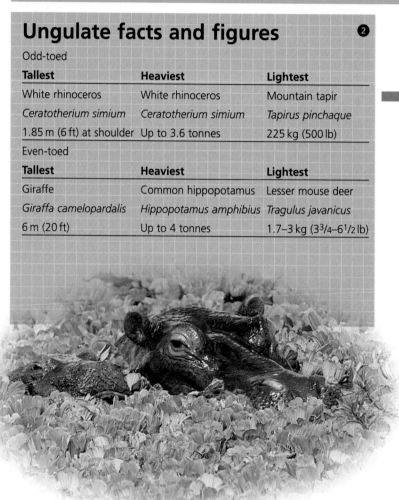

WATER HORSE The common hippopotamus is only distantly related to horses. Unlike its forest-dwelling cousin, the pygmy hippo (*Hexaprotodon liberiensis*), it spends most of its time in the water, emerging only after darkness to graze on land.

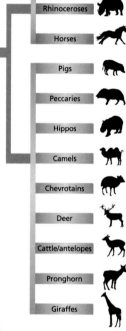

Tapirs
Rhinoceroses
Horses
Pigs
Peccaries
Hippos
Camels
Chevrotains
Deer
Cattle/antelopes
Pronghorn
Giraffes

FAMILY TREE
There are 12 families of hoofed mammal in two orders. By far the largest family is the family Bovidae, which contains all 110 species of cattle, antelopes, goats and sheep.

Tie-breaker
❸

Q: How many species of rhinoceros are there?
A: Five. The Sumatran rhino is the smallest living species, followed by the Javan, the Indian and then the black rhino. The white rhino is the largest. Like the black rhino, it comes from Africa.

⭐ **531**

Choice cuts
Hoofed mammals provide most of the **meat** that we eat. Domestic cows, pigs, sheep and goats are bred in numbers that vastly outweigh those of their wild counterparts. The USA alone is estimated to contain at least 100 million cattle and 50 million pigs at any one time.

Horns and antlers ❹

Horns and antlers are used by male ruminants for fighting. They are also used for defence against predators and in many species females have them too. Cattle, antelopes, sheep, goats and giraffes have permanent horns with a bony core. Deer have antlers of bone which are shed every year.

BLOOD SHED A moose (*Alces alces*, below) chews the velvet from his antlers. Velvet supplies growing antlers with blood.

RECORD BREAKER Asia's wild water buffalo (*Bubalus arnee*, inset below) has the longest horns of any animal.

Herd instinct ❺

Most hoofed mammals live under the constant threat of attack. To reduce the chances of being surprised by predators most live in herds – more eyes make it harder for hunters to sneak up on them.

Not all live in herds, however. Many forest-dwelling species, such as Africa's **duikers** (*Cephalophus* species) and **okapi** (*Okapia johnstoni*) are solitary for most of the time. They rely instead on camouflage and keeping quiet to avoid being eaten.

WALKING TALL The giraffe is one of the few hoofed mammals large enough to defend itself from lions.

WEIRD AND WONDERFUL ❻

In 1992 a **new species** of hoofed mammal was discovered. Dark brown with dagger-like horns, the vu quang ox, or saola (*Pseudoryx nghetinhensis*), lives in the dense and largely unexplored forests of Laos and Vietnam.

Living on leaves ❼

Compared with meat, leaves are low in nutrients and hard to digest. Hoofed mammals have evolved mechanisms to get the most out of what they eat. Ruminants all have a **four-chambered stomach**. The first chamber, the rumen, is where the process of digestion begins. Food is held there for several hours before being regurgitated for a second chewing. It is then swallowed again and passed into a different area of the intestine where digestion continues.

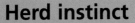

Elephants and their relatives

Core facts ❶

◆ Elephants, hyraxes and sea cows sprang from the same ancestral group. Elephants are classified into the order Proboscidea, hyraxes Hyracoidea and sea cows Sirenia.
◆ **Elephants** are the world's largest land animals. They are plant-eaters with brick-like molar teeth and a long trunk formed from the nose and upper lip.
◆ Elephants once ranged throughout Africa, Eurasia and North America. There are now just two species: the African elephant (*Loxodonta africana*) and Asian elephant (*Elephas maximus*).
◆ The African elephant has two subspecies: the savannah elephant (*L. a. africana*) and the smaller bush, or forest, elephant (*L. a. cyclotis*).
◆ There are 11 species of **hyrax** and four living species of **sea cow**. In one species, the **dugong**, the males have short tusks.

What's the difference? ❷

There are several ways to tell **African and Asian elephants** apart. African elephants have larger ears and a less rounded back. They also have a squarer head. Both male (bull) and female (cow) African elephants have large tusks, while female Asian elephants rarely have tusks at all. African and Asian elephants are actually not all that closely related. Asian elephants have more genes in common with woolly mammoths than with their modern cousins.

USEFUL TIPS Elephants have finger-like tips to their trunks. Asian elephants' trunks have one tip while African elephants' have two tips.

Land giant ❸

The **African elephant** is more than just the world's largest land mammal, it holds numerous other records too. Among them are owner of the world's largest ears and the largest teeth of any animal on land.
An elephant's tusks are modified incisors and the African elephant's may reach well over 3 m (10 ft) long.

The longest-lived land mammal apart from man is the Asian elephant, which may reach 78 years old.

Elephant errors ❹

Elephants are the subject of numerous myths. They do not go to elephant graveyards to die and they are not afraid of mice, for example. Whether or not they forget is hard to prove but they certainly have very good memories. Elephant herds are led by the eldest female, called the **matriarch**. In times of drought, her memory of where she has found food in the past often ensures the survival of the herd.

Tie-breaker ❺

Q: **What are the largest land animals to use tools?**
A: **Elephants.** Pieces of vegetation are often picked up with the trunk and used to swat flies or scratch an itch, for example. Elephants are the only animals apart from primates to throw objects at people or other creatures.

★ 489
Prehistoric pachyderms

Today's elephants are the most recent additions to a very long line. The earliest, *Moeritherium*, appeared about 40 million years ago. At least 120 different species are known to have existed since then. The **largest**, the steppe mammoth (*Mammuthus trogontherii*), was 4.5 m (15 ft) tall at the shoulder.

FLAT TEETH *Ambelodon* was the size of an Asian elephant. It lived in North America about 20 million years ago.

WEIRD AND WONDERFUL ❻

Elephants seem to have an understanding of death. When a herd member dies they 'grieve' and stay with the body for hours, protecting it. Relatives later return to its bones and spend time with them, as if in memory.

JUNGLE JUMBO Forest elephants are relatively small, rarely weighing more than three tonnes. It is these elephants that it is thought Hannibal used to cross the Alps.

SOCIAL LIFE Rock hyraxes live in groups of up to 26.

Hyraxes ❼

◆ Hyraxes look nothing like elephants but they are their closest land-living relatives. These rabbit-sized herbivores have little hooves instead of claws and long incisors which they use for fighting and defence.
◆ Hyraxes live in Africa and the Middle East (they appear in the Book of Psalms where they are referred to as 'conies').
◆ **Rock hyraxes**, or dassies (genus *Procavia*), live on rockfaces up to 4200 m (13 800 ft). **Bush hyraxes** (genus *Heterohyrax*) live in similar habitats but are confined to eastern Africa. **Tree hyraxes** (genus *Dendrohyrax*) are forest dwellers.

Sea cows ❽

Sea cows are the largest plant-eating aquatic mammals. Apart from the **dugong** (*Dugong dugong*), which is entirely marine, all are found in fresh, brackish and saltwater. The 6m (20 ft) long **Steller's sea cow** (*Hydrodamalis gigas*) from the Bering Sea was hunted to extinction in 1768.

GENTLE GRAZER The West Indian manatee (*Trichechus manatus*) occurs from Florida to the coast of Brazil.

ANSWERS

★ **29** It has a tusk ★

69 D: The killer whale ❷

135 C: World's biggest eyes ❷

137 D: The killer whale ❷

168 Baleen ❸

242 Breaching – fin whales are the largest to do this

341 Whale ❷❸❹

372 A sperm whale – author Herman Melville, 1851

683 Porpoises ❺

717 Dolphin ❺

786 True ❷

791 Humpback ❷

908 Orinoco ❼

916 Common dolphin ❺

927 Sperm whale (the others are all baleen whales) ❶

970 Delphinus – visible only in Northern Hemisphere

992 A dolphin ❼

Whales and dolphins

Core facts ❶

◆ Whales, dolphins and porpoises are born and spend their lives in the water. As **mammals**, they breathe air and give birth to live young which they suckle on milk.

◆ Whales, dolphins and porpoises make up the order Cetacea, which is split into two suborders: Odontoceti, which includes all toothed whales, and Mysticeti, which contains the baleen whales.

◆ **Toothed whales** include dolphins, porpoises and sperm whales. All are active hunters.

◆ **Baleen whales** are all filter feeders. They include the four largest animals: in descending order the blue whale, fin whale (*Balaenoptera physalus*), bowhead whale and right whale.

BLUE WHALE *Balaenoptera musculus*
The largest animal on Earth.

33.5 m (110 ft)

SPERM WHALE
Physeter macrocephalus
The world's largest predator and fifth largest animal.

18 m (60 ft)

HUMPBACK WHALE
Megaptera novaeangliae
The eighth largest animal and most studied baleen whale.

15 m (50 ft)

KILLER WHALE *Orcinus orca*
The world's largest species of dolphin. Males can weigh up to 9 tonnes.

7 m (23 ft)

HECTOR'S DOLPHIN *Cephalorhynchus hectori*
The shortest cetacean. The finless porpoise (*Neophocaena phocaenoides*) is slightly lighter.

1.2 m (4 ft)

Record breakers ❷

Whales hold many of the records in the animal kingdom including a few less than obvious ones.

◆ The bowhead whale (*Balaena mysticeus*) has the world's **biggest mouth**. Fully open, it is large enough to swallow a minibus.

◆ The **longest fins** of any animal belong to the humpback whale. At around 4.6 m (15 ft) its pectoral fins, or flippers, are almost twice as long as those of any other whale.

◆ The record for the **deepest dive** by an air-breathing animal is held by the sperm whale. Tagged sperm whales have been recorded diving to 2000 m (6560 ft) and indirect evidence suggests that they may sometimes reach depths of more than 3000 m (9840 ft).

◆ The sperm whale also has the world's **heaviest brain** at around 8 kg (17 lb 9 oz).

◆ The world's **biggest baby** is born to the **blue whale**. It measures 6–8 m (20–26 ft) long and weighs 2–3 tonnes at birth.

Baleen whales ❸

Most large whales feed on small prey, sieved from the water by plates of **baleen**, or whalebone, which hang down from the upper jaw. Baleen plates are fringed with long hair-like structures, which trap prey inside the mouth but allow water to be pushed out through them before the whale swallows.

The most common baleen whale species is the minke whale (*Balaenoptera acutorostrata*), which grows to 10 m (33 ft) long. The smallest, the pygmy right whale (*Caperea marginata*), reaches just 6.5 m (21 ft 6 in).

SOUP STRAINERS A humpback whale shows its baleen as it sweeps up a giant mouthful of food and water.

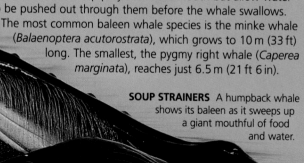

★ **29**

The narwhal

The tusk of the male narwhal (*Monodon monoceros*) is the **largest tooth** of any marine animal, in extreme cases growing to more than 3 m (10 ft) long. One in 30 females have tusks and one in 500 males sport two. The tusks are used by males for jousting to establish dominance in the social hierarchy.

Dorsal fin

FAMILIAR SMILE
The bottlenose dolphin (*Tursiops truncatus*) is the species most commonly kept in dolphinaria. In the wild, it is found in temperate and tropical ocean waters.

Beak

Pectoral fin, or flipper

Dolphins and porpoises ❺

Half of the world's cetaceans are sea-living dolphins and porpoises. Apart from the blackfish (pilot whales and their relatives) all dolphins have an obvious 'beak' – a feature that separates them from porpoises.

Most coastal dolphins and porpoises live in tightly knit groups of 2–12 individuals which often work together to catch prey. Oceanic dolphins usually travel in larger herds. Some species, such as the Atlantic white-sided dolphin (*Lagenorhynchus acutus*), may form herds over 1000 strong.

WEIRD AND WONDERFUL ❹

The **right whale** (*Balaena glacialis*) was given its common name by whalers. Unlike other large whales, it was easy to approach and floated after death, making it the 'right whale' to kill.

Tie-breaker ❻

Q: Where is a dolphin's blow-hole?
A: On the top of its head. The blow-hole is the equivalent of our nostrils. Unlike our nostrils however, it is controlled by powerful muscles and can be held tightly shut.

River dolphins ❼

Six species of cetacean live in fresh water. Two of those, the tucuxi (*Sotalia fluviatilis*) and finless porpoise also occur in the sea. True river dolphins include the Indus and Ganges river dolphins (*Platanista minor* and *P. gangetica*), and the baiji (*Lipotes vexillifer*), which lives in the Yangtze river.

DOWN RIVER The boto (*Inia geoffrensis*) is the largest river dolphin. It lives in the Amazon and Orinoco rivers.

Fluke

Lower primates

Core facts ❶

◆ Lower primates include **lemurs**, **lorises**, **pottos**, **bush-babies** and **tarsiers**. Also known as prosimians, literally 'before monkeys', they make up 35 of the 181 species in the order Primates; the other 146 are all monkeys or apes.
◆ All primates have **five grasping digits** on each limb and **forward-facing eyes**.

◆ All primates are either arboreal (tree living) or descended from arboreal ancestors. Apart from our own species, they live almost entirely in tropical or subtropical regions.
◆ Prosimians are the most primitive living primates. The two halves of their lower jaw are not fused together, unlike in most mammals.

Tarsiers ❷

◆ With gigantic eyes (each weighing as much as the brain) and swivelling ears, tarsiers are among the most bizarre-looking of all mammals.
◆ They are nocturnal insect-eaters and little bigger than mice, but incredibly agile, leaping between branches in almost pitch darkness.
◆ There are three species, two from Indonesia and one from the Philippines. Each can turn its head 360° and look directly backwards.

Bush-babies ❸

So called because of the crying sound that they make, bush-babies are Africa's equivalent of the tarsiers. Agile, nocturnal primates that feed mostly on insects, they differ from tarsiers in having thick, **bushy tails** and a **tooth-comb** – something they share with lemurs, pottos and lorises. There are six species, four are found only in rain forest while the other two inhabit wooded savannah.

Tie-breaker ❺

Q: What type of animal is an indri?
A: A lemur. The indri is the biggest living prosimian. Before humans reached Madagascar, however, it was just one of many large lemurs. The biggest of all – *Archaeoindris* – was the size of an orang-utan.

Lemurs ❹

Lemurs are found only on **Madagascar**. There are 22 species – before people arrived on the island about 2000 years ago there were at least 14 more. Lemurs have long snouts and most have whiskers. They include the **smallest primate**, the western rufous mouse lemur (*Microcebus murinus*).

SINGING FROM THE TREETOPS
Like many lemurs, the gibbon-sized indri (*Indri indri*) is endangered. The word lemur means 'ghost' in Malagasy.

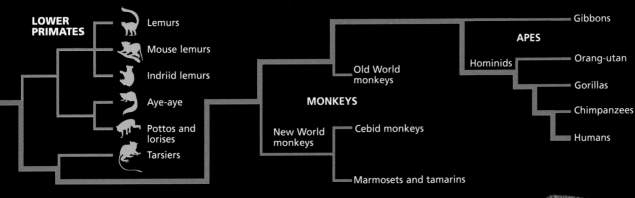

LOWER PRIMATES

- Lemurs
- Mouse lemurs
- Indriid lemurs
- Aye-aye
- Pottos and lorises
- Tarsiers

MONKEYS
- Old World monkeys
- New World monkeys
  - Cebid monkeys
  - Marmosets and tamarins

APES
- Gibbons
- Hominids
  - Orang-utan
  - Gorillas
  - Chimpanzees
  - Humans

FAMILY TREE None of the primates alive today are direct ancestors of humans but some are more closely related to us than others. The thick line represents the path from humans back to the common ancestor of all primates.

★ **89**

The aye-aye

Madagascar is an island without woodpeckers and the aye-aye has evolved to fill the niche they would usually occupy. It seeks out beetle grubs in wood by tapping bark with its long middle finger, listening carefully for the hollow sound of their tunnels with its huge, bat-like ears. When it finds a grub it gnaws through the wood and weedles it out with its spindly middle finger.

ENDANGERED SPECIES
The aye-aye is threatened by hunting and habitat loss.

Pottos and lorises

⑥

◆ These slow-moving creatures of the night creep through the branches of tropical forests in search of small prey such as insects. They also eat fruit and gums.

◆ There are two species of potto, both from **Africa**. The **golden potto**, or angwantibo (*Arctocebus calabarensis*) lives in west equatorial regions. The **potto** (*Perodicticus potto*) is more widespread.

◆ The two lorises come from **Asia**; the **slender loris** (*Loris tardigradus*) from India and Sri Lanka, and the **slow loris** (*Nycticebus coucang*) from tropical Southeast Asia.

CLOWN'S EYES The slow loris grows to about 30 cm (1 ft) long. Lorises were named by the Dutch; the word means 'clown' in their language.

Monkeys

Core facts ❶

◆ Monkeys are separated from primitive primates by subtle differences in skull structure and the fact that the two halves of their lower jaw are fused together. There are **107 species**.
◆ All 45 **Old World monkey** species belong to the family Cercopithecidae, which has two subfamilies: Cercopithecinae includes guenons, mangabeys, macaques mandrills and baboons; and Colobinae the colobus and leaf monkeys.
◆ The 62 species of **New World monkeys** are in two families. Callitrichidae contains the marmosets and tamarins; and Cebidae the sakis, titi, howler, spider, squirrel and woolly monkeys, capuchins, uakaris, muriqui and owl monkey.

Monkey facts and figures ❷

Old World		
Heaviest	**Lightest**	**Rarest**
Mandrill	Talapoin monkey	Tonkin snub-nosed monkey
Papio sphinx	*Miopithecus talapoin*	*Rhinopithecus avunculus*
54 kg (120 lb)	1.4 kg (3 lb 1 oz)	Fewer than 250

New World		
Heaviest	**Lightest**	**Rarest**
Muriqui	Pygmy marmoset	Muriqui
Brachyteles arachnoides	*Cebuella pygmaea*	*Brachyteles arachnoides*
15 kg (33 lb)	150 g (5¼ oz)	200–250

Old World, New World ❸

Old and New World monkeys have been evolving in isolation for more than 65 million years. Today, the two groups are separated by **three major differences**: New World monkeys have thumbs that oppose the palms of their hands rather than their index fingers; they have three rather than two premolar (grinding) teeth on each side of each jaw; and their nostrils open sideways.

NEW WORLD Nostrils face sideways.

Behaviour ❹

Monkeys as a group are almost all **diurnal**; the only nocturnal species is the owl monkey, or douroucouli (*Aotus trivirgatus*), which lives in the Amazon rain forest. Day-living has enabled monkeys to develop facial expressions to communicate emotions. It has also led to an increase in social activity, which in turn has driven the evolution of larger brains to keep track of who is who and one's own place in the hierarchy.

MONKEYING AROUND India's common, or Hanuman, langurs (*Semnopithecus entellus*) are as at home on the ground as they are in the trees.

OLD WORLD Nostrils face downwards.

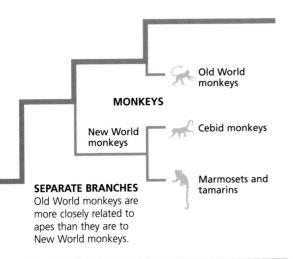

SEPARATE BRANCHES
Old World monkeys are more closely related to apes than they are to New World monkeys.

MONKEYS

Old World monkeys

New World monkeys

Cebid monkeys

Marmosets and tamarins

Mandrills and baboons ❺

◆ The **largest** monkeys, mandrills and baboons spend most of their time on the ground and retreat to the trees only when danger threatens.
◆ They live in male-dominated troops of 20–80 individuals. Males are much larger than females and are armed with long canine teeth which they flash when threatened.
◆ There are **five species**, all from Africa. The savannah and guinea baboons (*Papio cynocephalus* and *P. papio*) live in wooded grassland. The hamadryas baboon (*P. hamadryas*) inhabits rocky desert, while the drill (*P. leucophaeus*) and larger mandrill live in rain forest.

BOLD LOOK The male mandrill is the world's most colourful mammal. Females look similar but duller.

Marmosets and tamarins ❻

South and Central America's marmosets and tamarins are the world's **smallest** monkeys. Tree-living omnivores, they are the only higher primates with claws instead of fingernails, enabling them to scurry up and down rain forest trunks with ease despite their diminutive size.

Marmosets and tamarins are social animals, living in family groups consisting of a mated pair and their offspring. All but one species, Goeldi's marmoset (*Callimico goeldii*), usually give birth to twins, which are cared for by both parents. Often the male carries the babies around and hands them over to their mother for suckling.

Marmosets and tamarins include some of the rarest primates; 12 of the 21 species are classified as vulnerable or endangered by the IUCN (World Conservation Union).

LITTLE MONKEY At 14 cm (5½ in) long with a 20 cm (8 in) tail, the pygmy marmoset is the smallest monkey of all.

★ 735

Imperial apes

Apart from humans, the **Barbary apes** (*Macaca sylvanus*) of Gibraltar are Europe's only free-ranging primates. The apes (actually tailless macaque monkeys) were introduced from North Africa in the 1740s for game hunting. Legend has it that should they die out Gibraltar will cease to be part of the British Empire. In order to avert this they were topped up with new recruits in 1943 on the orders of Winston Churchill.

WEIRD AND WONDERFUL ❼
Vervet monkeys (*Cercopithecus aethiops*) seem to enjoy alcohol. Troops introduced to the Caribbean have developed such a taste for fermenting sugar cane that they have taken to raiding bars to steal unguarded drinks.

Apes

Core facts ❶

◆ Apes are the largest and most intelligent members of the order Primates. Unlike monkeys and primitive primates, they **have no tail**. There are two families: Hylobatidae (the gibbons), and Hominidae – the great apes (gorillas, chimps and orang-utans) and humans.
◆ **Gibbons** occur throughout tropical Southeast Asia. There are nine species.

◆ **Orang-utans** live in the forests of Sumatra and Borneo. There are two species.
◆ **Gorillas** are the largest living primates. There are two species, both from Africa.
◆ The two species of **chimpanzee** come from Africa. They live in groups of 15–120. Males work together to defend territory and hunt.
◆ There is one living species of **human**.

Gorillas ❷

Although **forest-dwellers**, gorillas spend most of their time **on the ground**. The eastern gorilla (*Gorilla beringei*) is split into three subspecies, of which the mountain gorilla (*G. b. beringei*) is the largest. The western gorilla (*Gorilla gorilla*) has two subspecies.

PLANT-EATER Gorillas live on the leaves and stems of ground plants. Like all apes, they are active only by day.

Gibbons ❸

◆ Gibbons are the **smallest apes** and the most highly adapted to life in the trees.
◆ They move through the branches by swinging from their arms, using their hands as hooks, and reach speeds of 16 km/h (10 mph).
◆ Gibbons feed mainly on young leaves and soft, pulpy fruits. They live in family groups of a monogamous pair and their young. Pairs hold territories and advertise their ownership of them by singing, often in unison.
◆ Different species have different songs: after birdsong these are among the most complex vocalisations in the entire animal kingdom.

★ 474

Silverbacks

Gorilla groups are made up of several females and their young led by one mature, silverback male. Silverbacks may weigh 275 kg (605 lb) – twice the weight of adult females. Male gorillas develop their silvery saddle at around 10 years of age.

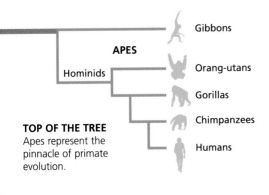

APES

Gibbons

Hominids

Orang-utans

Gorillas

Chimpanzees

Humans

TOP OF THE TREE
Apes represent the pinnacle of primate evolution.

Chimpanzees ❺

Chimpanzees are **our closest living relatives**, sharing nearly 99 per cent of our DNA. Like us, they use tools and are highly intelligent. They also have the capacity for language, learning signs developed for use by the deaf. Forest animals, chimps are split into two species, the familiar chimpanzee (*Pan troglodytes*) and the bonobo, or pygmy chimpanzee (*Pan paniscus*). Both feed on fruit and leaves, although the former also eats meat.

INGENIOUS APE A young chimp uses a stick to transport water to its mouth.

Orang-utans ❹

The Sumatran orang-utan (*Pongo abelii*) is the **largest tree-living** animal – adult males can weigh 90 kg (200 lb). The Bornean orang-utan (*P. pygmaeus*) is slightly smaller. Both species can live to about 60 years old.

Orang-utans are mainly **solitary**, apart from mothers with young, which stay together for up to 10 years. **Herbivores**, they eat a wide range of fruit and leaves which they collect from the branches. Their long, powerful limbs have hook-like fingers to help them move through the trees.

CLOSE RELATIVE A young girl uses a cone to transport ice cream to her mouth.

PRECIOUS BABY Orang-utans have a very low reproductive rate for wild animals. This youngster is one of just three or four its mother is likely to raise in her lifetime.

The human animal ❽

Human beings (*Homo sapiens*) are the world's **most successful large mammal**, living in virtually every habitat and on every continent. In recent history our species' population has exploded; during the past century alone the number of humans on the planet tripled.

The success of humankind is often attributed to our **bipedal** stance, which freed up our hands to create and manipulate tools. But it is also due in large part to our ability to communicate information and ideas; as well as having the **largest brain** compared to body size we also have the most highly developed vocal apparatus.

Tie-breaker ❼

Q: What type of ape is a siamang?
A: A gibbon. The siamang (*Hylobates syndactylus*) is the largest species of gibbon. Found on Sumatra and the Malay Peninsula, it has an inflatable throat-sac which acts as a resonator, amplifying its calls.

Animals in agriculture

A brief history ❶

◆ The first animals to be herded by people were probably **sheep** and **goats**. Evidence suggests that the domestication of these animals began at least 10 000 years ago. The herding of cattle came later, but by 2000 BC these animals too were domesticated.

◆ **Selective breeding** of farm animals is a more recent phenomenon. Most breeds of cattle, sheep, goats and pigs that we see today have an ancestry of just a few hundred years.

◆ Selective breeding continues with the goal of producing ever larger or **more productive** livestock. Over the past century the process has yielded significant results. For example, in 1925 the average chicken laid 100 eggs a year. Today the majority lay at least twice that number.

NORTHERN EXPOSURE The Highland cow is native to Scotland. Two centuries ago most were black, but today almost all are dun or red.

Cattle ❷

◆ Domesticated cattle are split into two species – *Bos taurus* includes all breeds with a European origin and *Bos indicus* the humped African and Asian breeds.

◆ All European breeds of cattle are descended from the now-extinct **aurochs** (*Bos primigenius*), which survived in south-eastern Europe until 1627.

◆ The origin of *Bos indicus* is less certain. Some zoologists believe they were domesticated from the kouprey (*Bos sauveli*) of Cambodia and Laos. Others think that *Bos indicus* was itself once a wild animal that now exists only in its domesticated form.

◆ There are 277 recognised breeds of domesticated cattle. Twelve of the most familiar are listed below.

Breed	Country of origin	Dairy or beef	Extra information
Aberdeen Angus	Scotland	Beef	
Beefmaster	USA	Beef	A Brahman-Hereford-Shorthorn cross that is a favourite breed with US ranchers
Brahman	India	Dairy	The original Hindu sacred cow, this breed has a large shoulder hump and floppy ears
Charolais	France	Beef	
Dairy Shorthorn	England	Dairy	
Friesian/Holstein	The Netherlands	Dairy	The world's most popular dairy breed
Galloway	Scotland	Beef	
Hereford	England	Beef	
Jersey	Channel Islands, UK	Dairy	The world's second most common dairy breed: produces very creamy milk
Limousin	France	Beef	
Simmenthal	Switzerland	Beef	
South Devon	England	Beef	The largest and leanest British breed

SADDLEBACKS
Pigs may have as many as 14 piglets in a litter. The smallest piglet is known as the runt.

Pigs

❸

Pigs were domesticated from the wild boar (*Sus scrofa*) around 5000 years ago. The development of most modern pig breeds began in the 18th century.

Breed	Country of origin	Pork or bacon	Other information
Berkshire	England	Pork	Large black breed with white snout and 'socks' to the knees
Chester white	USA	Bacon	
Gloucester Old Spot	England	Pork	
Hampshire	USA	Both	
Landrace	Denmark	Bacon	America, Belgium, Britain, The Netherlands, Finland, France, Germany, Italy, Norway and Sweden all have their their own distinctive breeds of landrace developed from the original Danish stock
Large black	England	Both	
Large white (Yorkshire)	England	Bacon	Ears are erect rather than flopped forwards
Saddleback	England	Both	
Tamworth	England	Pork	
Vietnamese pot-bellied	Vietnam	Pork	A small breed, often kept as a pet outside its native country

★ 286

Goats

Throughout the world goats are kept mainly for milk. Goat's milk is easier to digest than cow's milk. Goats have a preference for shrubs over grasses, which enables them to survive in places where cattle cannot. A male goat is known as a billy and a female is known as a nanny. Baby goats are called kids.

MODERN-DAY COWBOYS
Argentinian gauchos drive a herd of Hereford cattle across Patagonia.

Sheep

❺

Domesticated sheep have existed for at least 10 000 years. Their wild ancestor, the mouflon (*Ovis orientalis*) still lives in the mountains of Asia Minor and southern Iran, and on the Mediterranean islands of Sardinia and Corsica.

Breed	Country of origin	Meat or wool	Other information
Cheviot	England	Meat	
Dorset down	England	Wool	
Jacob's sheep	Spain	Wool	Black and white: may have four horns
Lonk	England	Both	
Merino	Spain	Both	Popular in Australia and South Africa
Scottish blackface	Scotland	Wool	Hardy and aggressive. Both sexes horned
Soay	Scotland	Meat	The most primitive surviving breed of sheep, unchanged for at least 2000 years
Suffolk	England	Meat	
Welsh mountain	Wales	Both	
Wensleydale	England	Wool	Wool is long and curled into ringlets

Poultry

❹

The **chicken** is the world's most common bird. There are an estimated 10 billion on the planet at any one time; more than there are people. All chickens are descended from India's red junglefowl (*Gallus gallus*). Domestic **ducks** and **geese** have more than one ancestor; the **muscovy** duck is descended from the South American musk duck (*Biziura lobata*) and the **Aylesbury** duck from the mallard (*Anas platyrhynchos*), for example.

The numbers or star following the answers refer to information boxes on the right.

ANSWERS

19	**False** – they usually do, but not always
32	The Manx cat ❸
★ 36	Crufts ★
38	The King Charles spaniel ❷
39	India is George Bush's cat, Socks belonged to Clinton
75	The Pekingese ❷
177	The domestic cat ❶ ❸
193	**Dogs** – used in agility tests at dog shows ★
236	The domestic dog ❶ ❷
291	The greyhound ❷
318	**George Gordon Byron** – he also kept three monkeys
407	**False** (it was bred in Germany) ❷
471	**Gold** (goldfish) ❺
495	Mexico ❷
498	**The hamster** (from *hamstern*) ❻
507	Dogs ❶ ❷
577	**Cat's** – the cat's whiskers
662	Hutch ❻
674	**200** (there are actually 195) ❷
802	The mastiff ❷
850	Hamster ❻
942	**42** – 12 incisors, 4 canines, 16 premolars and 10 molars

Pets

Old companions ❶

Domestic dogs belong to the species *Canis familiaris* and are descended from the wolf (*Canis lupus*). Evidence for the domestication of dogs dates back around 10 000 years. The ancestry of **domestic cats** (*Felis catus*) goes back to the African wild cat (*F. silvestris libyca*).

Dogs

Dog breeds are divided into seven categories. **Gundogs** were bred to flush out and retrieve gamebirds. **Hounds** were bred for hunting, while **pastoral** dogs protected domestic animals.

Terriers were bred to hunt vermin. Most **toy dogs** were bred as pets. **Working dogs** include guard dogs and dogs used for search and rescue. **Utility** covers all dogs bred for a purpose other than those covered by sport or working categories. ❷

Gundogs
Bracco Italiano
Brittany
English Setter
German Longhaired Pointer
German Shorthaired Pointer
German Wirehaired Pointer
Gordon Setter
Hungarian Vizsla
Hungarian Wirehaired Vizsla
Irish Red and White Setter
Irish Setter
Italian Spinone
Kooikerhondje
Large Munsterlander
Nova Scotia Duck Tolling Retriever
Pointer
Retriever (Chesapeake Bay)
Retriever (Curly Coated)
Retriever (Flat Coated, right)
Retriever (Labrador)
Spaniel (American Cocker)
Spaniel (Clumber)
Spaniel (Cocker)
Spaniel (English Springer)
Spaniel (Field)
Spaniel (Irish Water)
Spaniel (Sussex)
Spaniel (Welsh Springer)
Spanish Water Dog
Weimaraner

Hounds
Afghan Hound
Basenji
Basset Bleu De Gascogne
Basset Fauve De Bretagne
Basset Griffon Vendeen (Grand)
Basset Griffon Vendeen (Petit)
Basset Hound
Bavarian Mountain Hound
Beagle
Bloodhound (right)
Borzoi
Dachshund (Long Haired)
Dachshund (Miniature Long Haired)
Dachshund (Smooth Haired)
Dachshund (Miniature Smooth Haired)
Dachshund (Wire Haired)
Dachshund (Miniature Wire Haired)
Deerhound
Elkhound
Finnish Spitz
Foxhound
Grand Bleu De Gascogne
Greyhound
Hamiltonstovare
Ibizan Hound
Irish Wolfhound
Otterhound
Pharaoh Hound
Rhodesian Ridgeback
Saluki
Segugio Italiano
Sloughi
Whippet

Pastoral dogs
Anatolian Shepherd Dog
Australian Cattle Dog
Australian Shepherd
Bearded Collie
Belgian Shepherd Dog (Groenendael)
Belgian Shepherd Dog (Laekenois)
Belgian Shepherd Dog (Malinois)
Belgian Shepherd Dog (Tervueren)
Bergamasco
Border Collie
Briard
Collie (Rough)
Collie (Smooth)
Estrela Mountain Dog
Finnish Lapphund
German Shepherd Dog (Alsatian)
Hungarian Kuvasz
Hungarian Puli
Komondor
Lancashire Heeler
Maremma Sheepdog
Norwegian Buhund
Old English Sheepdog (above)
Polish Lowland Sheepdog
Pyrenean Mountain Dog
Pyrenean Sheepdog
Samoyed
Shetland Sheepdog
Swedish Lapphund
Swedish Vallhund
Welsh Corgi (Cardigan)
Welsh Corgi (Pembroke)

Terriers
Airedale Terrier
Australian Terrier
Bedlington Terrier
Border Terrier
Bull Terrier
Bull Terrier (Miniature)
Cairn Terrier
Cesky Terrier
Dandie Dinmont Terrier
Fox Terrier (Smooth)
Fox Terrier (Wire, left)
Glen of Imaal Terrier
Irish Terrier
Kerry Blue Terrier
Lakeland Terrier
Manchester Terrier
Norfolk Terrier
Norwich Terrier
Parson (Jack) Russell Terrier
Scottish Terrier
Sealyham Terrier
Skye Terrier
Soft Coated Wheaten Terrier
Staffordshire Bull Terrier
Welsh Terrier
West Highland White Terrier

Toy dogs
Affenpinscher
Australian Silky Terrier
Bichon Frise
Bolognese
Cavalier King Charles Spaniel (right)
Chihuahua (Long Coat)
Chihuahua (Smooth Coat)
Chinese Crested Dog
Coton De Tulear
English Toy Terrier (Black and Tan)
Griffon Bruxellios
Havanese
Italian Greyhound
Japanese Chin
King Charles Spaniel
Lowchen (Little Lion Dog)
Maltese
Miniature Pinscher
Papillon
Pekingese
Pomeranian
Pug
Yorkshire Terrier (world's **smallest breed** – the smallest individual ever measured 6.3 cm (2½ in) at the shoulder and weighed 113 g (4 oz) when fully grown)

Utility dogs
Boston Terrier
Bulldog
Canaan Dog
Chow Chow
Dalmatian
French Bulldog
German Spitz (Klein)
German Spitz (Mittel)
Japanese Akita
Japanese Shiba Inu
Japanese Spitz
Keeshond
Lhasa Apso
Mexican Hairless
Miniature Schnauzer
Poodle (Miniature)
Poodle (Standard, right)
Poodle (Toy)
Schipperke
Schnauzer
Shar Pei
Shih Tzu
Tibetan Spaniel
Tibetan Terrier

Working dogs
Alaskan Malamute
Beauceron
Bernese Mountain Dog
Bouvier Des Flandres
Boxer
Bullmastiff
Canadian Eskimo Dog
Doberman
Dogue de Bordeaux
Giant Schnauzer
Great Dane (world's **tallest breed**, measuring up to 105 cm (41½ in) at the shoulder)
Greenland Dog
Hovawart
Leonberger
Mastiff (world's **heaviest breed**, weighing up to 155 kg (343 lb))
Neapolitan Mastiff
Newfoundland (pictured)
Pinscher
Portuguese Water Dog
Rottweiler
St. Bernard
Siberian Husky
Tibetan Mastiff

Cats

The earliest evidence for the existence of domestic cats comes from **Ancient Egypt**, where they had religious significance, as well as practical importance as guardians of grain stores. By the tenth century AD cats had arrived in England, and from there they travelled to North America with the first settlers in the 17th century.

Shorthaired cats

Abyssinian	British Cream Shorthair	Exotic Shorthair	Rex
American Shorthair	British Smoke Shorthair	Foreign Shorthairs	Russian Blue
American Wirehair	British Spotted Shorthair	(many colours)	Scottish Fold
Bengal	British Tabby Shorthair	Havana	Siamese
Bombay	British Tipped Shorthair	Japanese Bobtail	Singapura
British Bicolour Shorthair	British Tortoiseshell Shorthair	Korat	Snowshoe
British Black Shorthair	British White Shorthair	Manx	Sphynx
British Blue Shorthair (pictured)	Burmese	Ocicat	Tonkinese
British Blue-Cream Shorthair	Burmilla	Oriental Shorthairs	
	Egyptian Mau	(many colours)	

Longhaired cats

Angora	Chocolate Longhair	Golden Longhair	Smoke Longhair
Balinese	Chocolate	Golden Tabby	Somali
Bicolour Longhair	Tortoiseshell	Golden Torbie	Tabby Longhair
Birman	Colourpoint	Lilac Longhair	Tiffany
Black Longhair	Longhair	Lilac-Cream Longhair	Tortoiseshell Longhair
Blue Longhair	Cream	Maine Coon	Tortoiseshell-and-White
Blue-Cream Longhair	Longhair	Norwegian Forest Cat (left)	Longhair
Cameo Longhair	Cymric	Pewter Longhair	Turkish Van Cat
Chinchilla Longhair		Ragdoll	White Longhair
		Red Self Longhair	

❸

WEIRD AND WONDERFUL

❹ The **Jack Russell terrier** is named after the man who created the breed. Jack Russell, a parson from Devonshire, developed his terrier in the early 1800s to flush foxes from their earths. Today's Jack Russells are all descended from his stock.

New models ❺
Some pets are changed from the animals they are descended from, but can still interbreed with them.

Pet	Wild ancestor	Place of origin	Difference from ancestor
Budgie	Budgerigar (*Melopsittacus undulatus*)	Central Australia	Colour (all wild budgerigars are yellow and green)
Canary	Island canary (*Serinus canaria*)	Canary Islands	Colour (island canaries are yellow and black)
Ferret	European polecat (*Mustela putorius*)	Britain and Europe	Colour (wild polecats are dark brown)
Goldfish	Wild goldfish (*Carassius auratus*)	Europe and Asia	Body shape and colour (wild goldfish start life grey)
Guinea pig	Cavy (*Cavia tschudii*)	Central Andes, South America	Colour (cavies are brown) and length of fur

Wild animals in the home ❻
Many animals that we think of as pets are identical to their ancestors, which still live in the wild.

Pet	Wild ancestor	Place of origin
Chinchilla	Chinchilla (*Chinchilla laniger*)	Central Andes, South America
Cockatiel	Cockatiel (*Nymphicus hollandicus*)	Northern and eastern Australia, New Guinea
Cockatoo	Sulphur-crested cockatoo (*Cacatua galerita*)	Australia
Gerbil	Mongolian gerbil, or jird (*Meriones unguiculatus*)	Mongolia
Grey parrot	Grey parrot (*Psittacus erithacus*)	Tropical western and central Africa
Hamster	Golden hamster (*Mesocricetus auratus*)	Syria
Mynah bird	Hill mynah (*Gracula religiosa*)	Southern Asia
Rabbit	Common rabbit (*Oryctolagus cuniculus*)	Mediterranean Europe

ALL BITE AND NO BARK The Basenji hound is the only breed of dog that does not bark. It is not mute but makes a distinctive sound all of its own, officially described as a mixture of a chortle and a yodel.

★ 36

Pooches on parade

Crufts is the world's best-known dog show, and one of its biggest. Held annually at the National Exhibition Centre (NEC) in Birmingham, England, it attracts more than 20 000 entrants. Categories range from obedience to flyball, where teams of dogs race over hurdles in a relay using a tennis ball for a baton.

Working animals

A life of labour ❶

◆ The majority of domestic animals were tamed to provide food, clothing or power.
◆ Some animals supply all three – the **yak** (*Bos mutus*), for instance, is kept for its milk, meat, wool and use as a beast of burden.
◆ Others are kept just as work animals. The **donkey**, domesticated from the African wild ass (*Equus africanus*) and the **horse**, developed from races of the Eurasian wild horse (*Equus caballus*), are two such examples.
◆ The sterile offspring of horse and donkey, the **mule** (or hinny where the father is a horse and mother a donkey) is used almost exclusively as a pack animal.

Horses for courses ❷

Since the horse was first domesticated it has been bred into a greater variety of shapes and sizes than any other animal apart from the dog. The **largest** breed, the **shire horse**, can reach over 21 hands (2.1 m/7ft – measured to the withers) and weigh 1.5 tonnes (3350 lb). By contrast the smallest miniature horse bred to date measured just 3$\frac{1}{2}$ hands (36 cm, or 14 in) and weighed 9 kg (20 lb).

The majority of horse breeds were developed for use as **riding animals**. For some, such as the **Arab**, the main criterion selected for was speed. For others it was power. Most heavy horses, including the shire, trace their ancestry back to medieval war horses, such as the English Black Horse, which were bred to carry knights in full armour. Later, these horses were turned to the cart or plough, which before were pulled by oxen.

WEIRD AND WONDERFUL ❸

In parts of Siberia **reindeer** are ridden like horses. The semi-domesticated animals are kept by the Nenet people, who also use them to carry packs and draw sledges, and provide them with milk, hides and meat.

HORSE POINTS Several words have been coined over the years to describe different parts of a horse's body, some of which are listed here. Gaskin and hock apply only to the back legs.

Croup
Loin
Hindquarters
Tailhead
Gaskin
Hock
Cannon
Fetlock
Pastern
Hoof

Animals in war

Hannibal's elephants are famous animals of war but they are not the only ones. The Roman army bred **mastiff dogs** for battle and **horses** were used for centuries to carry soldiers into conflict. Today **dolphins** and **seals** are used by the US Navy to seek out mines.

RIDING HIGH Camel racing is popular in Arabian countries. The camels used are dromedaries (*Camelus dromedarius*).

Animals in sport ❹

Racing animals has been popular for thousands of years. The earliest references to horse racing date back to Ancient Egypt and the sport was part of the ancient Olympic Games. More recently, horses have been joined by greyhounds, pigeons and sled dogs. Equestrian sports have branched out to include showjumping, carriage driving and three-day eventing.

Withers

Mane

Beasts of burden ❺

In the West horses have long been the main working animals. Elsewhere, however, other species have been domesticated for the purpose. In the Andes the **llama** (*Lama glama*) is the principal pack animal, while in the Himalayas it is the **yak** and in Mongolia the **bactrian camel** (*Camelus bactrianus*).

PADDY PLOUGHER A domesticated water buffalo (*Bubalus arnee*) helps prepare a Chinese paddy field.

Knee

Cannon

Tie-breaker
❻

Q: Which South American animal gave rise to the domesticated llama and alpaca?
A: The guanaco (*Lama guanicoe*). The guanaco's best-known descendant, the llama, was once used for food and leather as well as carrying loads. The alpaca (*Lama pacos*) has always been kept just for its fine wool.

Fetlock

Pastern

QUESTION NUMBER

The numbers or star following the answers refer to information boxes on the right.

ANSWERS

4	**Jonah** ❷
45	**Snakes** ❹
111	**A donkey** ❷
152	**The unicorn** ❺
171	**A dove** ❷
172	**An elephant** ❸
173	**The sacred ibis** ❹
174	**The owl** ❹
178	**Francis of Assisi** – founded the Franciscan holy order
179	**A monkey** ❸
★ 180	**All of them** (Jains are vegetarian) ★
233	**A wolf** ❹
241	**A squirrel** ❼
270	**Daniel** ❷
412	**Lion** (half-lion) ❺
423	**Great Sphinx** ❹
537	**The pig** ★
748	**Saint Patrick** – the patron saint of Ireland
860	**Manticore** ❺

Animals in religion and myth

Global phenomenon ❶

◆ Animals appear in the religions and mythology of virtually every culture on Earth.
◆ In **Australia** the Aboriginal Dreamtime was populated by the eternal ancestors who wandered the Earth sometimes in animal form.
◆ In **Japan** the Shinto religion is based around nature worship, while in **Canada**, the Inuit tell how the world was created by a raven.
◆ Animal gods exist in Hinduism and were common in extinct religions. In **Europe**, the Celts had the horned god Cernunnos, the Ancient Greeks Pan, and the Vikings Audhumla, the primeval cow who nourished the frost giant Ymir at the beginning of time.

Nature of faith ❷

◆ In religious texts, such as the Bible, animals often symbolise good or evil.
◆ The **Christian** concept of Original Sin stems from the story of Eve's temptation by a serpent in the Garden of Eden. Elsewhere the Lamb of God is used as a metaphor for Christ.
◆ Animals also appear in Biblical stories and parables, such as those of Daniel in the lion's den, and Jonah and the whale. The tale of Noah and the Ark appears in the Bible, the Torah (**Judaism**) and the Koran (**Islam**).
◆ Most of the great eastern religions feature animals. The concept of karma and rebirth are common to **Buddhism** and **Hinduism**. Evil deeds committed in this life increase the chances of being reborn as an animal – the worse the deeds, the more lowly the species.

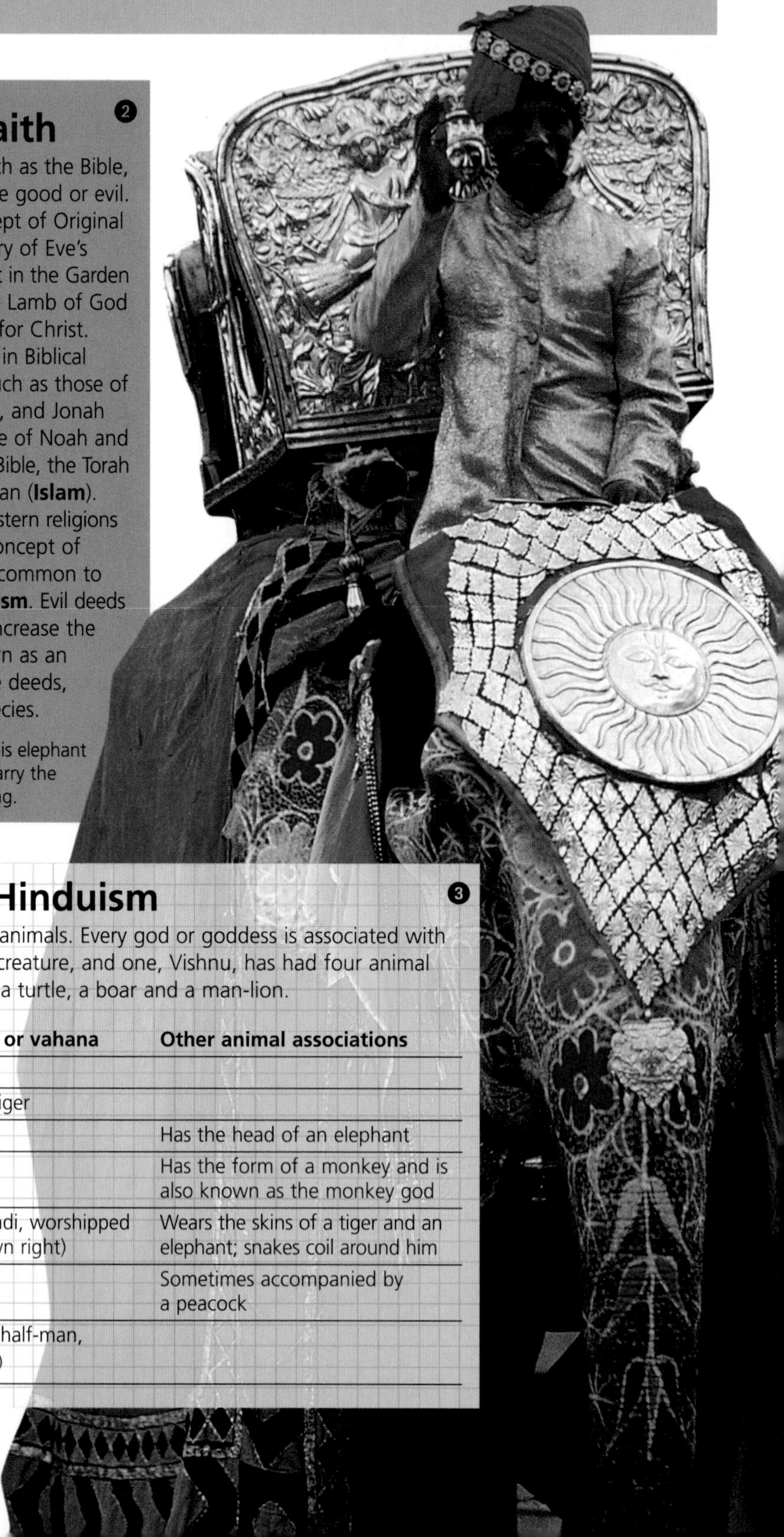

CEREMONIAL STEED This elephant has been dressed up to carry the groom to a Hindu wedding.

Animals in Hinduism ❸

Hinduism is filled with animals. Every god or goddess is associated with at least one particular creature, and one, Vishnu, has had four animal incarnations; as a fish, a turtle, a boar and a man-lion.

Deity	Vehicle, or vahana	Other animal associations
Brahma	Eagle	
Durga	Lion or tiger	
Ganesh	Mouse	Has the head of an elephant
Hanuman		Has the form of a monkey and is also known as the monkey god
Siva, or Shiva	Bull (Nandi, worshipped in his own right)	Wears the skins of a tiger and an elephant; snakes coil around him
Saraswathi	Swan	Sometimes accompanied by a peacock
Vishnu	Garuda (half-man, half-bird)	

FOUR SONS OF HORUS Each protected an organ after mummification. Qebehsenuef (left) guarded the intestines, and Duamutef (next to him) the stomach. Baboon-headed Ha'py watched over the lungs and Imsety the liver.

Egyptian and Classical beasts ❹

The Ancient Egyptian pantheon was filled with gods of half-animal form. **Horus** had the head of a falcon, **Anubis** the head of a jackal, and **Thoth** the head of an ibis; a bird held sacred by the people.

The Ancient Greeks created monsters whose names we still recognise: **centaurs**, who were half-man, half-horse; the many-headed snake **Hydra**; and the winged horse **Pegasus**. Their gods also sometimes took animal form. Zeus appeared both as a bull and a swan, for example. Roman mythology was filled with animals; their god of the countryside, **Faunus**, gave us the word fauna.

★ 180

Taboo food

In several religions certain meats are considered taboo. Jews and muslims do not eat the flesh of pigs and hindus are forbidden to harm cows or eat beef. Buddhism forbids the killing of animals but not the eating of meat. Buddhists can eat meat provided the animal was killed by somebody else.

WEIRD AND WONDERFUL ❻

Dragons occur in the mythologies of many cultures. In eastern Asia they were associated with abundance, prosperity and good fortune. In medieval Europe they represented martial might but also sin, heresy and the Devil.

Viking and Celtic myths ❼

◆ The two major ancient cultures of northern Europe each had rich mythologies populated by numerous fabulous beasts.
◆ Among the viking monsters was **Fenrir**, a gigantic wolf destined to kill Odin, the chief of the gods, and the squirrel **Ratatosk**, who transported messages up and down Yggdrasil, the cosmic ash tree that intersected the realms of the frost giants, gods and mortals.
◆ Birds played a central role in Celtic mythology. Morrigan, the goddess of war, was believed to take the form of a crow, and heroes frequently turned into eagles in tales of their exploits. Another creature that often appeared in Celtic tales was the salmon, the most famous being the **Salmon of Knowledge** from Irish mythology.

Medieval monsters ❺

Some fabulous beasts were peculiar to medieval England. Books of natural history from the time – **bestiaries** – included animals both real and invented. Some of the monsters they listed had their roots in Classical accounts but others appear nowhere else.

Name	Description	Additional information
Amphisbaena	Reptile with a head at either end of its body	Had glowing eyes and did not shirk the cold
Basilisk	King of the serpents	Could kill with a glance
Bonnacon	Bovine animal with inward-curling horns	Fired a flammable liquid at attackers from its anus
Caladrius	All-white bird	Could foretell whether a sick man would die
Jaculus	Small, winged serpent	Ambushed livestock
Leucrota	Bred from a hyena and a lioness	Mouth stretched to its ears; had strips of bone in place of teeth
Parandus	Ox-sized with antlers and a shaggy coat	Could change colour to match its background
Seps	Venomous snake	Venom could destroy both flesh and bone
Serra	Sea creature with huge wings	Enjoyed racing against ships
Yale	Horse-sized and black with an elephant's tail	Had the jaws of a boar and two horns which it could move independently

FIRE BIRD The phoenix lived for five hundred years before being burned and reborn from the flames. Its existence was quoted in bestiaries as evidence for the credibility of the resurrection of Christ.

HORNED HORSE The unicorn was believed in throughout Eurasia, with specific mention made of it in early Taoist writings.

LEONINE LEANINGS The griffin (left) had the head, body and wings of an eagle and the hindquarters of a lion. The manticora, or manticore (below), had the head of a man and the body of a lion.

ANSWERS

34	**Border collie** ❷
77	**An owl** (specifically a snowy owl) ❸
222	**Sylvester Stallone** – born 1946
265	**A coyote** (Wile E Coyote) ❺
303	**A warthog** ❷
305	**Elsa** ❷
306	***Gorillas in the Mist*** – with Sigourney Weaver
308	**An orang-utan** ❸
309	**A frog** ❹
★ **312**	**David Attenborough** ★
381	***The Fly*** – a sequel, *The Fly II*, followed in 1989
386	**A moth** – the chrysalis of a death's head hawk moth
403	**True** ❷
434	**Michael Crichton** – also wrote *Prey*, 2002
435	**Nick (Nicolas) Park** – also created *Chicken Run*
721	**A pig** ❷
743	**Kaa** – he was a python
774	**The groundhog** – in *Groundhog Day*, 1993
933	**An iguanodon** – a large dinosaur of the Jurassic and Cretaceous periods

Animals on screen

Life in two dimensions ❶

Nowadays more people are familiar with Donald and Daffy than mallard or mandarin (they are all ducks in case you were wondering). Television and cinema are the main source of entertainment for the majority of the world's population. The former is also the main point of contact with the natural world for many people, particularly those of us who live in cities.

Making it in the movies ❷
The A-list of animal stars.

PIG WITH ASPIRATIONS
Babe dreamed of being a sheepdog.

Character	Type of animal	Film titles
Babe	Pig	*Babe* (1995), *Babe: Pig in the City* (1998)
Bambi	Fawn	*Bambi* (1942)
Beethoven	St. Bernard dog	*Beethoven* (1992), *Beethoven's 2nd* (1993)
Dumbo	Elephant	*Dumbo* (1940)
Elsa	Lion	*Born Free* (1966)
Flik	Ant	*A Bug's Life* (1998)
Francis the Talking Mule	Mule	*Francis Goes to the Races* (1951) and others
Ginger	Chicken	*Chicken Run* (2000)
Gromit	Dog	*A Grand Day Out* (1989), *The Wrong Trousers* (1993)
Jaws	Great white shark	*Jaws* (1975), *Jaws 2* (1978), *Jaws 3-D* (1983), *Jaws 4 – The Revenge* (1987)
King Kong	Gorilla	*King Kong* (1933, remade 1976), *King Kong Vs. Godzilla* (1963)
Lassie	Shetland sheepdog	*Lassie Come Home* (1943) and others
Mighty Joe Young	Gorilla	*Mighty Joe Young* (1949, remade 1998)
Rin Tin Tin	Alsatian dog	*Jaws of Steel* (1927)
Rocky	Rooster	*Chicken Run* (2000)
Roger Rabbit	Rabbit	*Who Framed Roger Rabbit?* (1988)
Simba	Lion	*The Lion King* (1994), *Lion King II: Simba's Pride* (1998)
Stuart Little	Mouse	*Stuart Little* (1999)
Willy	Killer whale	*Free Willy* (1993)
Z	Ant	*Antz* (1998)

HMMM…
Gromit ponders Wallace's trousers.

Best supporting animal ❸
Creature co-stars and the people they played alongside.

Character	Animal	Supported	In
Baby	Leopard	Katherine Hepburn and Cary Grant	*Bringing Up Baby* (1938)
Cheta	Chimpanzee	Johnny Weissmuller	*Tarzan the Ape Man* (1932)
Clyde	Orang-utan	Clint Eastwood	*Every Which Way But Loose* (1978)
Diablo	Horse	Warner Baxter	*In Old Arizona* (1928)
Hedwig	Snowy Owl	Daniel Radcliffe	*Harry Potter and the Philosopher's Stone* (2001)
Hooch	Dog	Tom Hanks	*Turner and Hooch* (1989)
Sandy	Dog	Aileen Quinn	*Annie* (1982)
Toto	Dog	Judy Garland	*The Wizard of Oz* (1939)

Stars of the small screen

Some were real, some were models and some were puppets. A few are on TV today.

Character	Type of animal	Television programme or series
Ben	Grizzly bear	*Gentle Ben*
Black Beauty	Horse	*Black Beauty*
Champion	Horse	*Champion the Wonder Horse*
Flipper	Bottle-nosed dolphin	*Flipper*
Fozzie	Bear	*The Muppet Show*
Kermit	Frog	*The Muppet Show*
Mister Ed	Horse	*Mister Ed the Talking Horse*
Paddington Bear	Bear	*Paddington, The Adventures*
Pingu	Penguin	*Pingu*
Robin (Kermit's nephew)	Frog	*The Muppet Show*
Rowlf	Dog	*The Muppet Show*
Sam	Eagle	*The Muppet Show*
Shaun	Sheep	*A Close Shave* (Aardman Animations)
Silver	Horse	*The Lone Ranger*
Skippy	Grey kangaroo	*Skippy the Bush Kangaroo*

SILVER SCREEN SILVERBACK King Kong atop the Empire State Building in the 1933 RKO stop-motion animation classic.

★ 312

Lions in the living room

Nature documentaries are a staple ingredient for television programmers today, but 50 years ago they did not exist. The genre was pioneered by the BBC. David Attenborough, younger brother of film director Richard, got in at the beginning, starting his career with *Zoo Quest* in 1954.

Cartoon creatures ❺

It is hard to imagine Disney without Mickey Mouse. Below are some of the most famous cartoon animals ever to grace our screens.
Studio abbreviations: CH=Cosgrove/Hall, D=Disney, HB=Hanna-Barbera, S=Spumco, T=Terrytoons, WB=Warner Brothers

BEARS IN TIES Yogi and Booboo lived in Jellystone National Park.

Type of creature	Character (studio)
Bear	Yogi and Booboo (HB)
Cat	Felix (various), Sylvester (WB), Stimpy (S), Tom (HB)
Chihuahua	Ren (S)
Cockerel (Rooster)	Foghorn Leghorn (WB)
Coyote	Wile E Coyote (WB)
Dog	Deputy Dawg, Droopy (HB), Goofy (D), Hong Kong Fooey (HB), Muttley (HB), Pluto (D), Scooby-doo (HB)
Duck	Daffy (WB), Donald (D)
Mouse	Danger Mouse (CH), Jerry (HB), Mickey Mouse (D), Mighty Mouse (T), Speedy Gonzales (WB)
Pig	Porky (WB)
Rabbit	Bugs Bunny (WB)
Roadrunner	Roadrunner (WB)
Striped skunk	Pepé Le Pew (WB)
Tasmanian devil	Taz (WB)

Animals in the arts

Natural subjects ❶

Animals frequently appear either as subjects in paintings or characters in literature. The oldest known artworks are images of animals – cave paintings dating back more than 20 000 years show various creatures, many of which no longer exist.

Animals also feature in song titles, poetry or as themes for novels or stage productions.

Beastly books ❷
Ten bestsellers with animals in their titles.

Book	Author	Published	Further information
Day of the Jackal	Frederick Forsyth	1970	Made into a film starring Edward Fox
Do Androids Dream of Electric Sheep?	Philip K. Dick	1968	This most celebrated of Dick's 45 science fiction novels was filmed as *Blade Runner*
Maribou Stork Nightmares	Irvin Welsh	1995	The Scottish author's third published book
Of Mice and Men	John Steinbeck	1937	Made into a film starring John Malkovich
The Horse Whisperer	Nicholas Evans	1995	Made into a film starring Robert Redford
The Rats	James Herbert	1974	The horror writer's first published novel
The Snow Goose	Paul Gallico	1941	One of the world's most popular children's books
The Wasp Factory	Iain Banks	1984	First novel; Banks also wrote *The Crow Road*
To Kill a Mockingbird	Harper Lee	1960	One of the three top-selling novels of all time
Wild Swans	Jung Chang	1992	Winner of the 1992 NCR Book Award

Fur and feathers in fiction ❸
Characters from five of the world's best-known animal novels.

Book	Author	Character and animal
Animal Farm	George Orwell	Benjamin (donkey), Boxer, Clover, Mollie (horses) Jessie (dog), Moses (Raven), Muriel (goat), Napoleon, Old Major, Snowball, Squealer (pigs)
Moby Dick	Herman Melville	Moby Dick (sperm whale)
Tarka the Otter	Henry Williamson	Tarka (otter)
The Jungle Book	Rudyard Kipling	Akela (wolf), Bagheera (panther), Baloo (bear), Kaa (snake), Raksha (wolf), Rikki-tikki-tavi (mongoose), Shere Khan (tiger)
The Lion, The Witch and The Wardrobe	C.S. Lewis	Aslan (lion)

FIRST EDITION Made internationally famous by Disney's 1967 animated film, Rudyard Kipling's *The Jungle Book* was first published in 1894.

Animals in paintings

Five famous works of art that feature animals.

Artwork	Artist	Animal
Guernica	Pablo Picasso	Bull
Surprise! A Storm in the Forest	Henri Rousseau	Tiger
The Goldfish	Paul Klee	Goldfish
The Monarch of the Glen	Sir Edwin Landseer	Red deer stag
The Physical Impossibility of Death in the Mind of Someone Living	Damien Hirst	Tiger shark

SURPRISE! Rousseau's most famous work, this painting hangs in the National Gallery, London.

DANCING BUNNY Peter Rabbit in the Frederick Ashton ballet *Tales of Beatrix Potter*.

Opera, ballet and musicals

There have been countless productions with animal themes. Below are five of the best known.

Title	Genre	Composer	Further information
Cats	Stage musical	Andrew Lloyd Webber	The world's longest-running musical: closed on May 11, 2002, exactly 21 years after it opened
Die Fledermaus	Operetta	Johann Strauss	First performed in 1875 (The Bat)
Madame Butterfly	Opera	Giacomo Puccini	First performed in 1904
Swan Lake	Ballet	Pyotr Ilyich Tchaikovsky	This classic was poorly received when it premiered in 1877 in Moscow
The Thieving Magpie	Opera	Gioacchino Rossini	One of more than 30 operas by the Italian

Chart toppers

The following songs with animals in the titles were all Top 40 hits in Britain and the USA.

Single	Artist/Band	Released
Bat out of Hell	Meat Loaf	1978
Buffalo Soldier	Bob Marley and the Wailers	1983
Butterflies	Michael Jackson	2002
Crocodile Rock	Elton John	1973
Eye of the Tiger	Survivor	1982
Free as a Bird	The Beatles	1995
Hound Dog	Elvis Presley	1956
Hungry Like the Wolf	Duran Duran	1982
Karma Chameleon	Culture Club	1983
The Love Cats	The Cure	1983
Rat Trap	Boomtown Rats	1978
Union of the Snake	Duran Duran	1983
When Doves Cry	Prince	1984

★ 311

Aesop's fables

Aesop is thought to have been born a slave in Greece in the 6th century BC. He is credited with over 650 fables, including *The Fox and the Grapes* and *The Tortoise and the Hare*.

The Owl and the Pussy-cat went to sea
In a beautiful pea-green boat,
EDWARD LEAR • 1812-1888

Poetry

NO NONSENSE Lear's poems remain popular today.

Work	Poet	Year	Poem or collection
Crow	Ted Hughes	1971	Both
Death of a Naturalist	Seamus Heaney	1966	Poem
The Owl and the Pussycat	Edward Lear	1867	Poem
The Raven	Edgar Allen Poe	1845	Poem
The Thought-Fox	Ted Hughes	1957	Poem
The Tyger	William Blake	1794	Poem
The Windhover	Gerard Manley Hopkins	1918	Poem
To the Skylark	William Wordsworth	1875	Poem
Walrus and the Carpenter	Lewis Carroll	1871	Poem
Wolfwatching	Ted Hughes	1989	Collection

Animal symbolism

The right image ❶

◆ Animal symbolism appears in every language and culture. The English language is full of animal references; to feel bullish or be as quiet as a mouse, for example. Visual symbols are everywhere – on cars, outside banks, on clothes.
◆ In language and in branding, animals are often used to encapsulate desirable characteristics, such as strength or speed. They are also used to represent places. National flags and coats of arms often contain creatures associated with the country – the Mexican flag features a rattlesnake being killed by an eagle, while the coat of arms for the Ivory Coast is emblazoned with the head of a bush elephant.

Sporting connections ❷

Many sports have name associations with animals, nowhere more so than in American football.

NFL Football Teams	Major League Baseball Teams	International Rugby Teams
Arizona Cardinals	Arizona Diamondbacks	Argentina (The Pumas)
Atlanta Falcons	Baltimore Orioles	Australia (The Wallabies)
Baltimore Ravens	Detroit Tigers	British Lions
Carolina Panthers	Florida Marlins	South Africa
Chicago Bears	St Louis Cardinals	(The Springboks)
Cincinnati Bengals	Tampa Bay Devil Rays	USA (Eagles)
Denver Broncos	Toronto Blue Jays	
Detroit Lions		
Indianapolis Colts		
Jacksonville Jaguars		
Miami Dolphins		
Philadelphia Eagles		
St Louis Rams		
Seattle Seahawks		

★ 738

Place names

Most places named after animals were christened by settlers moving in from afar. Such names are particularly common in the Americas; the Cayman Islands, Cape Cod and Buffalo in the USA, and Moose Jaw and Red Deer in Canada are just a few.

Brands and advertising ❸

Various creatures have become associated with companies through advertising over the years: the toucan with Guinness, for example, and the tiger with Esso. Several international companies use animals in their logos.

Company	Animal
Bacardi (rum)	Bat
Barclays Bank	Eagle
HMV	Jack Russell terrier
Lloyds/TSB	Black Horse
Martell (cognac)	Swallow
Merrill Lynch	Bull
MGM (film)	Lion
Qantas (airline)	Kangaroo

EUROPEAN FIRM
Puma was founded in Germany in 1948.

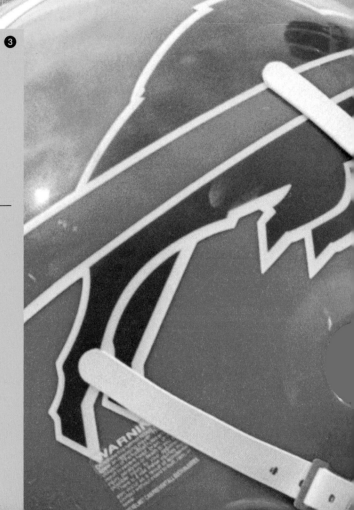

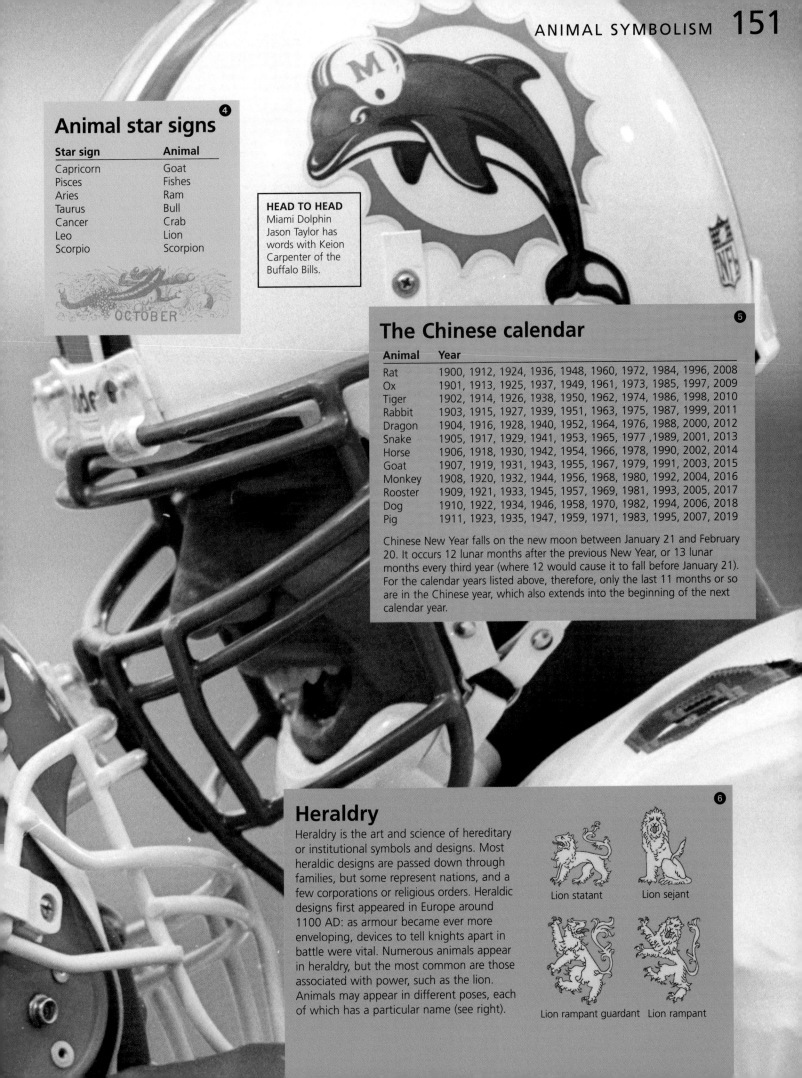

Animal star signs ④

Star sign	Animal
Capricorn	Goat
Pisces	Fishes
Aries	Ram
Taurus	Bull
Cancer	Crab
Leo	Lion
Scorpio	Scorpion

OCTOBER

HEAD TO HEAD
Miami Dolphin
Jason Taylor has
words with Keion
Carpenter of the
Buffalo Bills.

The Chinese calendar ⑤

Animal	Year
Rat	1900, 1912, 1924, 1936, 1948, 1960, 1972, 1984, 1996, 2008
Ox	1901, 1913, 1925, 1937, 1949, 1961, 1973, 1985, 1997, 2009
Tiger	1902, 1914, 1926, 1938, 1950, 1962, 1974, 1986, 1998, 2010
Rabbit	1903, 1915, 1927, 1939, 1951, 1963, 1975, 1987, 1999, 2011
Dragon	1904, 1916, 1928, 1940, 1952, 1964, 1976, 1988, 2000, 2012
Snake	1905, 1917, 1929, 1941, 1953, 1965, 1977, 1989, 2001, 2013
Horse	1906, 1918, 1930, 1942, 1954, 1966, 1978, 1990, 2002, 2014
Goat	1907, 1919, 1931, 1943, 1955, 1967, 1979, 1991, 2003, 2015
Monkey	1908, 1920, 1932, 1944, 1956, 1968, 1980, 1992, 2004, 2016
Rooster	1909, 1921, 1933, 1945, 1957, 1969, 1981, 1993, 2005, 2017
Dog	1910, 1922, 1934, 1946, 1958, 1970, 1982, 1994, 2006, 2018
Pig	1911, 1923, 1935, 1947, 1959, 1971, 1983, 1995, 2007, 2019

Chinese New Year falls on the new moon between January 21 and February
20. It occurs 12 lunar months after the previous New Year, or 13 lunar
months every third year (where 12 would cause it to fall before January 21).
For the calendar years listed above, therefore, only the last 11 months or so
are in the Chinese year, which also extends into the beginning of the next
calendar year.

Heraldry ⑥

Heraldry is the art and science of hereditary
or institutional symbols and designs. Most
heraldic designs are passed down through
families, but some represent nations, and a
few corporations or religious orders. Heraldic
designs first appeared in Europe around
1100 AD: as armour became ever more
enveloping, devices to tell knights apart in
battle were vital. Numerous animals appear
in heraldry, but the most common are those
associated with power, such as the lion.
Animals may appear in different poses, each
of which has a particular name (see right).

Lion statant   Lion sejant

Lion rampant guardant   Lion rampant

The human impact

Population pressure ❶

◆ Over the last few centuries the world's human population has expanded at an incredible rate – there are more people in China today than there were on the whole planet 150 years ago.
◆ One result of this explosive growth has been the disappearance of wilderness and wild animals as land has been turned over to agriculture. Habitat fragmentation and hunting have also had a major impact. Many species have become extinct but, thanks to the efforts of conservationists, some that would otherwise have gone for good are still with us today.

Conservation organisations ❷

Organisation	International Headquarters	Country of origin	Web site
Audubon Society	New York, USA	USA	www.audubon.org
Greenpeace	Amsterdam, The Netherlands	USA	www.greenpeace.org
IUCN	Gland, Switzerland	International	www.iucn.org
Royal Society for the Protection of Birds (RSPB)	Sandy, England	England	www.rspb.org
WWF	Gland, Switzerland	England	www.wwf.org

Captive breeding ❸

Zoos once existed just to entertain but today they have a much more important role as refuges for endangered species. Several species of animal owe their existence to zoos. The **Arabian oryx** (*Oryx leucoryx*), hunted to extinction in the wild by 1972, is back in its desert home after captive breeding by zoos in Phoenix and San Diego, USA. **Père David's deer** (*Elaphurus davidiensis*), exterminated in China by 1894, has also been reintroduced to the wild after being bred at London Zoo.

Numerous captive breeding programmes continue today. One of the more prestigious should soon see the reintroduction of the **golden lion tamarin** (*Leontopithecus rosalia*) to Brazil.

SAVED Extinct in the wild by 1987, the California condor (*Gymnogyps californianus*) is back in the skies after captive breeding.

Preserving wilderness ❹

Straddling the borders of Montana and Wyoming, USA, **Yellowstone National Park** is famous for its geysers and spectacular scenery. What is less commonly known is that when it was set aside by President Ulysses Grant in 1872, it was the world's first ever national park.

The creation of Yellowstone set a trend that was soon being followed outside the US. In 1879 the **Royal National Park** was created by the government of New South Wales, Australia, making it the world's second national park. Six years later **Banff National Park** was established in Alberta, Canada.

WILD HERD American bison, or buffalo (*Bison bison*), roam free today in Yellowstone National Park.

Conservation pioneers **5**

Nature conservation is a relatively recent concept. The first conservation organisations appeared at the end of the 19th century – **George Bird Grinnell** formed the Audubon Society in 1886 – but it was not until the mid-20th century that the movement really began to gather pace. One of the trail-blazers was **Sir Peter Scott**. He founded the Wildfowl and Wetlands Trust at Slimbridge in England in 1946 and became the first chairman of the World Wildlife Fund (now called simply WWF) in 1961. Scott also designed the World Wildlife Fund's original panda logo.

Joining Scott at the birth of the World Wildlife Fund was the first Director General of UNESCO, **Sir Julian Huxley**. Grandson of the influential Darwinist Thomas Huxley and brother of author Aldous Huxley, he had also helped to found IUCN – the International Union for the Conservation of Nature and Natural Resources, also known as the World Conservation Union.

Many other men and women played important roles in the growth of the conservation movement but two in particular stand out from the crowd. **Gerald Durrell**, who awakened an interest in animals for many through his books, opened Jersey Zoo in 1959, simultaneously creating the Durrell Wildlife Conservation Trust. And Professor **David Bellamy**, known mainly from his television appearances, co-founded The Conservation Foundation in 1982.

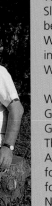

GREAT LOSS Gerald Durrell with one of the critically endangered red ruffed lemurs (*Varecia variegata rubra*) reared at Jersey Zoo. Sadly, Gerald Durrell passed away in 1995. His widow, Lee, continues the work of the Durrell Wildlife Conservation Trust.

National parks and reserves **6**

Below are 20 of the world's most important sanctuaries for wildlife.

Park	Country (state or region)
Amboseli National Park	Kenya
Banff National Park	Canada (Alberta)
Bialowieza National Park	Poland
Blue Mountains National Park	Australia (New South Wales)
Corbett National Park	India
Doñana National Park	Spain
Etosha National Park	Namibia
Everglades National Park	USA (Florida)
Fjordland National Park	New Zealand (South Island)
Gir Forest National Park	India (Gujurat)
Kakadu National Park	Australia (Northern Territory)
Kruger National Park	South Africa
Manu Biosphere Reserve	Peru
Masai Mara National Reserve	Kenya
Ranthambor National Park	India (Rajasthan)
Royal Chitwan National Park	Nepal
Serengeti National Park	Tanzania
Torres del Paine National Park	Chile
Tsavo National Park	Kenya
Yosemite National Park	USA (California)

★ 691

US giant

San Diego Zoo and Wildlife Park cover nearly 1900 acres (770 hectares) and are home to over 7000 animals. The Zoo has existed since 1916 and the Wildlife Park, where herds of animals roam free in enormous enclosures, since 1972.

Defining rare **8**

The **IUCN** (World Conservation Union) groups rare animals into one of four main categories. Lower risk species are threatened but in less danger of extinction than vulnerable species. They in turn are less at risk than endangered species. Critically endangered species face an immediate risk of extinction.

WEIRD AND WONDERFUL **7**

Some animals have gained from human migration and population growth. Creatures that live off our crops, such as the **house sparrow** (*Passer domesticus*), have expanded in numbers alongside ourselves.

The page number in brackets indicates where you will find the questions for each quiz.

Quiz 0 (page 8)

1 Snakes
2 Beavers
3 The tongue
4 Jonah
5 The African elephant
6 Fangs
7 Earthworms
8 Canines
9 The walrus
10 Sharks

Quiz 1 (page 8)

11 False
12 True
13 False
14 True
15 False
16 True
17 False
18 False
19 False
20 False

Quiz 2 (page 8)

21 In the Arctic
22 The emperor penguin
23 Lemmings
24 Ermine
25 The polar bear
26 Antlers
27 The Arctic tern
28 Arctic fish
29 It has a tusk
30 Blubber

Quiz 3 (page 8)

31 The dingo
32 The Manx cat
33 A roar
34 Border collie
35 Alpha
36 Crufts
37 A fox
38 The King Charles spaniel
39 India is President Bush's cat, Socks belonged to Clinton
40 A sabretoothed cat

Quiz 4 (page 9)

41 The cheetah
42 A mammal
43 Stag beetles
44 Aries
45 Snakes
46 Turtles
47 A stock market
48 A jellyfish
49 Lion
50 Spiders

Quiz 5 (page 9)

51 The Andes
52 A red deer stag
53 The goat
54 Eagles
55 They are all the same animal
56 Snow leopard
57 Sheep
58 Rabbits and hares
59 The chamois
60 Spain

Quiz 6 (page 9)

61 D
62 C
63 B
64 A
65 A
66 A
67 B
68 A
69 D
70 B

Quiz 7 (page 10)

71 Armadillos
72 Australia
73 Rabbits
74 The ostrich
75 The Pekingese
76 Its tail
77 An owl
78 *Cats*
79 The lion
80 T Rex

Quiz 8 (page 10)

81 Koala
82 Sloth
83 Camouflage
84 Albino
85 Lobster
86 Krill
87 Talon
88 Mammal
89 Aye-aye
90 Marlin

Quiz 9 (page 10)

91 A beetle
92 Workers
93 Locusts
94 Moths
95 The Crickets
96 Their eggs
97 Asthma
98 Blood
99 Woodlice
100 Ants

Quiz 10 (page 10)

101 Plankton
102 Whiskers
103 Giant squid
104 Dogfish
105 Termites
106 Albatross
107 Mudskipper
108 Echidnas
109 Trilobites
110 Tubeworms

Quiz 11 (page 11)

111 A donkey
112 Kid
113 The bongo
114 Don Quixote
115 Sancho Panza
116 George
117 An antelope
118 Buck
119 The deer and the antelope
120 Caligula

Quiz 12 (page 11)

121 Theodore Roosevelt
122 Gander
123 A mollusc
124 Beekeepers
125 Africa
126 Forest man
127 Afrikaans
128 Ferret
129 The chinchilla
130 Fish lizard or fish reptile

Quiz 13 (page 11)

131 A
132 C
133 C
134 A
135 C
136 A
137 D
138 B
139 D
140 D

Quiz 14 (page 12)

141 Snake
142 Ostrich
143 Scorpion
144 Koala bear
145 Beetle
146 Wolf
147 Chainmail armadillo
148 Slug
149 Centipede
150 Rabbits

Quiz 15 (page 12)

151 The African elephant
152 The unicorn
153 A parasite lives on a host
154 Frogs
155 Troop
156 Mother-of-pearl
157 The whale shark
158 Fingernails
159 A horse and a donkey
160 They regurgitate them as pellets

Quiz 16 (page 12)

161 Meat
162 The giant panda
163 Omnivore
164 The wolf
165 Scavenger
166 Termites
167 The chimpanzee
168 Baleen
169 Fish
170 Swallow it whole

Quiz 17 (page 12)

171 A dove
172 An elephant
173 The sacred ibis
174 The owl
175 Lion
176 The Aztecs
177 The domestic cat
178 Francis of Assisi
179 A monkey
180 All of them

Quiz 18 (page 13)

181 Snowy owl
182 Orang-utan
183 Pheasant
184 Flamingo
185 Crocodile
186 Zebra
187 Elephant
188 Snake
189 Tiger
190 Peacock

Quiz 19 (page 14)

191 Fish
192 Horses
193 Dogs
194 Butterfly
195 Horse
196 Camels
197 The eagle (Philadelphia Eagles)
198 A hare
199 Racing pigeons
200 A rabbit punch

Quiz 20 (page 14)

201 Duck
202 North America
203 Guernsey or Jersey
204 The goose
205 Vietnam
206 A cockerel
207 Cow
208 On its legs
209 A duck
210 Pig

Quiz 21 (page 14)

211 True
212 True
213 True
214 True
215 True
216 False
217 True
218 False
219 False
220 False

Quiz 22 (page 14)

221 Richard the First
222 Sylvester Stallone
223 Tiger (Tiger Woods)
224 Adam Ant
225 Jack Nicklaus
226 Erwin Rommel
227 Fish
228 Carlos the Jackal
229 Niki Lauda
230 Charlie Parker

Quiz 23 (page 15)

231 Peregrine falcon
232 The lion
233 A wolf
234 The cow
235 The brown rat
236 The domestic dog
237 The garden snail
238 The hippopotamus
239 Vespa
240 Sheep

Quiz 24 (page 15)

241 A squirrel
242 Breaching
243 On the front
244 Fruit
245 They are the only
    venomous lizards
246 Africa and Asia
247 The Housemartins
248 Panama
249 Lek
250 Baa Baa Black
    Sheep

Quiz 25 (page 15)

251 B
252 A
253 B
254 D
255 C
256 B
257 B
258 D
259 A
260 B

Quiz 26 (page 16)

261 The giraffe
262 One
263 Elton John
264 Rain forest
265 A coyote
266 Birds
267 Seashells
268 Canada
269 A blackbird
270 Daniel

Quiz 27 (page 16)

271 Tuna
272 Clam
273 Sardines
274 Prawns
275 Lobster
276 Oyster
277 Anchovy
278 Haddock
279 Mackerel
280 Monkfish

Quiz 28 (page 16)

281 Honeybees
282 A marten
283 Bird's nest soup
284 Aphids
285 North America
286 The goat
287 Lanolin
288 Fertiliser
289 Civet
290 A caterpillar

Quiz 29 (page 16)

291 The greyhound
292 Ford
293 The Beetle
294 The Golden Hind
295 The mallard
296 The spider
297 Kingfisher
298 Jaguar
299 The turtle
300 'Spruce Goose'

Quiz 30 (page 17)

301 A horse
302 Rabbits
303 A warthog
304 Flamingoes
305 Elsa
306 *Gorillas in the Mist*
307 A rat
308 An orang-utan
309 A frog
310 Brer Rabbit

Quiz 31 (page 17)

311 Aesop
312 David
    Attenborough
313 Charles Darwin
314 Chimpanzees
315 Fossils
316 Iain Banks
317 He classified the
    animal kingdom
318 George Gordon
    Byron
319 James Lovelock
320 Sir Stamford Raffles

Quiz 32 (page 17)

321 D
322 C
323 B
324 C
325 B
326 C
327 B
328 B
329 B
330 C

Quiz 33 (page 18)

331 The Eagles
332 Ravens
333 Flock
334 The Beatles
335 A marsupial
336 Nectar
337 The Andean condor
338 The puffin
339 Bats
340 The lämmergeier

Quiz 34 (page 18)

341 Whale
342 Teeth
343 Apes
344 Grassland
345 Coral
346 Jellyfish
347 Monkey
348 Parasite
349 Sloth
350 Seal

Quiz 35 (page 18)

351 Wildebeest
352 Jellyfish
353 Salmon
354 Beaches
355 Hibernation
356 Snow goose
357 Caribou
358 Nomadic
359 Monarch
360 Grey whales

Quiz 36 (page 18)

361 Clutch
362 Spawn
363 They balance them
    on their feet
364 Seahorses
365 The ostrich
366 Gills
367 The kiwi
368 400
369 Platypus or echidna
370 30 cm (1 ft)

Quiz 37 (page 19)

371 A pride
372 A sperm whale
373 France
374 Fleas
375 Insects
376 The mockingbird
377 Palomino
378 Sea lions
379 Smell
380 The emu

Quiz 38 (page 19)

381 *The Fly*
382 The black widow
383 Wood
384 Trapdoor spiders
385 Henrik Ibsen
386 A moth
387 Killer bees
388 Sydney
389 Scorpions
390 A beetle

Quiz 39 (page 19)

391 A
392 D
393 C
394 D
395 D
396 D
397 B
398 A
399 B
400 B

Quiz 40 (page 20)

401 False
402 True
403 True
404 True
405 True
406 True
407 False
408 True
409 True
410 False

Quiz 41 (page 20)

411 The chicken
412 Lion
413 Antarctica
414 A tiger
415 Beetles
416 Langoustine
417 The Minoan civilisation
418 It rolls into a ball
419 Spain
420 A cob

Quiz 42 (page 20)

421 Great Barrier Reef
422 Great tit
423 Great Sphinx
424 Great white shark
425 Great northern diver
426 Great grey owl
427 Great Bear
428 Great diving beetle
429 Great crested grebe
430 Great ape

Quiz 43 (page 20)

431 Regent's Park
432 Yellowstone
433 Exmoor
434 Michael Crichton
435 Nick (Nicolas)
436 The grey squirrel
437 Nepal
438 South Africa
439 Père David's deer
440 Corbett National Park

Quiz 44 (page 21)

441 Fish
442 Invertebrate
443 Mammal
444 Reptile
445 Reptile
446 Invertebrate
447 Fish
448 Reptile
449 Amphibian
450 Fish

Quiz 45 (page 22)

451 The giant panda
452 The bald eagle
453 The dove
454 Ferrari
455 A giraffe
456 A bat
457 A lion
458 A tiger
459 Miami
460 Puma

Quiz 46 (page 22)

461 Herd
462 Pack
463 Raft
464 Hover
465 Smack
466 Murmuration
467 Shrewdness
468 Murder
469 Crash
470 Mob

Quiz 47 (page 22)

471 Gold
472 Diamond
473 Money
474 Silver
475 Emerald
476 Silver
477 Gold
478 Ruby
479 Silver
480 Gold

Quiz 48 (page 22)

481 Ivory
482 Trunk
483 Hannibal
484 Sri Lanka
485 Matriarch
486 Pachyderm
487 Thailand
488 Musth
489 Mastodon
490 Hyraxes

Quiz 49 (page 23)

491 The wandering albatross
492 A salamander
493 Alaska
494 Yaks
495 Mexico
496 *Velociraptor*
497 Gorillaz
498 The hamster
499 Sloths
500 Bhutan or Wales

Quiz 50 (page 23)

501 Arachnophobia
502 Birds
503 Mice
504 Reptiles
505 Because they are afraid of fish
506 Bats
507 Dogs
508 Horses
509 Bees
510 Zoophobia

Quiz 51 (page 23)

511 B
512 C
513 D
514 C
515 D
516 A
517 B
518 D
519 B
520 A

Quiz 52 (page 24)

521 The females
522 A female fox
523 The males
524 Female
525 A ewe
526 The female
527 A male
528 The male
529 The males
530 Falconry

Quiz 53 (page 24)

531 Deer
532 Honey
533 Haggis
534 Sturgeon
535 The water buffalo
536 Squid
537 The pig
538 Taramasalata
539 Mussels
540 No

Quiz 54 (page 24)

541 Penguin
542 Tiger
543 Vulture
544 Albatross
545 Dinosaur
546 Goose
547 Toad
548 Bat
549 Armadillo
550 Mouse

Quiz 55 (page 24)

551 Panda
552 Moles
553 Birds
554 Six
555 The basilisk
556 A nest
557 Nutria
558 Ants
559 That it is poisonous
550 Neither

Quiz 56 (page 25)

561 Dorsal fin
562 Gills
563 Gill cover
564 Lateral line
565 Pectoral fin
566 Swim bladder
567 Pelvic fin
568 Muscle
569 Anal fin
570 Caudal fin

Quiz 57 (page 26)

571 Mouse
572 Coot
573 Possum
574 Glutton
575 Fox
576 Ox
577 Cat's
578 Ape
579 Wolf
580 Crow

Quiz 58 (page 26)

581 A shrew
582 None
583 They spend more time in trees
584 Hares
585 A bat
586 Tropical rain forest
587 Lions
588 Shell
589 Asexual reproduction
590 A chimpanzee

Quiz 59 (page 26)

591 Swallowtail
592 Cocktail
593 Wagtail
594 Dovetail
595 Fishtail
596 Ponytail
597 Oxtail
598 Cottontail
599 Mare's tail
600 Springtail

Quiz 60 (page 26)

601 Chameleons
602 Metamorphosis
603 Tadpoles
604 Caterpillars
605 Juvenile
606 Season
607 Elvers
608 Moulting
609 Sloughing
610 Ptarmigan

Quiz 61 (page 27)

611 True
612 True
613 True
614 True
615 True
616 True
617 True
618 False
619 True
620 True

Quiz 62 (page 27)

621 Its nose
622 Tree-living
623 Baboon
624 None
625 Evil
626 They thought it
was a French spy
627 South America
628 The rhesus macaque
629 It is the world's
largest monkey
630 It is nocturnal

Quiz 63 (page 27)

631 A
632 D
633 A
634 C
635 C
636 B
637 D
638 B
639 C
640 A

Quiz 64 (page 28)

641 Blue
642 Blue
643 Red
644 Blue
645 Red
646 White
647 Red
648 Red
649 Blue
650 Red

Quiz 65 (page 28)

651 Eight
652 Six
653 Two
654 Three
655 Ten
656 One
657 Eight
658 One
659 Two
660 None

Quiz 66 (page 28)

661 Aquarium
662 Hutch
663 Stable
664 Form
665 Holt
666 Aviary
667 Drey
668 Sett
669 Vespiary
670 Lodge

Quiz 67 (page 28)

671 Grassland animals
672 Moth
673 Mammals
674 200
675 Damselflies
676 An adult male
elephant
677 Hibernate
678 Aestivate
679 The giant squid
680 Our own species,
Homo sapiens

Quiz 68 (page 29)

681 Hedgehogs
682 Chipmunk
683 Porpoises
684 Chimpanzee
685 Colobus
686 Bush-babies
687 Virginia opossum
688 Leopard seal
689 Eland
690 Bowhead

Quiz 69 (page 29)

691 San Diego
692 They are at night
693 London Zoo
694 Kabul Zoo
695 Gerald Durrell
696 Barcelona Zoo
697 Zoological gardens
698 The Bronx
699 Seaworld
700 Melbourne

Quiz 70 (page 29)

701 B
702 A
703 D
704 D
705 A
706 C
707 C
708 A
709 B
710 B

Quiz 71 (page 30)

711 Seal
712 Tarantula
713 Moray
714 Eider
715 Midwife
716 Shark
717 Dolphin
718 Herd
719 Crab
720 Nocturnal

Quiz 72 (page 30)

721 A pig
722 To frighten
predators
723 Aphid
724 North and South
America
725 The lion
726 An albatross
727 A sponge
728 A monkey
729 Harem
730 Terrible reptile
or terrible lizard

Quiz 73 (page 30)

731 The kiwi
732 Africa
733 A kangaroo and
an emu
734 The bear
735 Gibraltar
736 Komodo
737 The springbok
738 Alberta
739 The Andean condor
740 South Africa and
Namibia

Quiz 74 (page 30)

741 The adder
742 Mexico
743 Kaa
744 Australia, or
Australasia
745 The Viper
746 Cobras
747 2001
748 Saint Patrick
749 By constriction
750 Africa

Quiz 75 (page 31)

751 Coral grouper
752 Gorilla
753 Giant panda
754 Hippopotamus
755 Tree frog
756 Scarlet macaw
757 Praying mantis
758 Eagle owl
759 Golden eagle
760 Crocodile

Quiz 76 (page 32)

761 The Northern
Hemisphere
762 Webbing
763 Russia
764 Alcatraz
765 They are animals
766 The Thames
767 In the deep sea
768 Cuttlefish (also
squid and
octopuses)
769 The Galapagos
770 Leeches

Quiz 77 (page 32)

771 Madagascar
772 Gibbon
773 In the sea
774 The groundhog
775 It is a forest animal
776 To lick up ants
777 The Boomtown Rats
778 No
779 The wombat
780 Johann Strauss

Quiz 78 (page 32)

781 True
782 False
783 True
784 True
785 True
786 True
787 True
788 False
789 True
790 False

Quiz 79 (page 32)

791 Humpback
792 Musk
793 Scent gland
794 Pit viper
795 Hammerhead
796 Antennae
797 Colour
798 Lateral line
799 Pheromones
800 Tarsier

Quiz 80 (page 33)

801 The tiger
802 The mastiff
803 The harrier
804 The Desert Rats
805 Carrier pigeons
806 Sea lions or dolphins
807 Foxhole
808 An eagle
809 Bearskins
810 The lynx

Quiz 81 (page 33)

811 A chimpanzee (or a great ape)
812 A snake
813 Parrot
814 The giraffe
815 Australia
816 A primitive primate
817 An anteater
818 South America
819 Nose-horned
820 Bats

Quiz 82 (page 33)

821 C
822 B
823 C
824 C
825 D
826 D
827 A
828 A
829 B
830 C

Quiz 83 (page 34)

831 Black
832 Black
833 White
834 Black
835 Black
836 White
837 Black
838 White
839 Black
840 Black

Quiz 84 (page 34)

841 Beaver
842 Prairie dog
843 Dormouse
844 Rabbit
845 Capybara
846 Water rat
847 Harvest mouse
848 Porcupine
849 Squirrels
850 Hamster

Quiz 85 (page 34)

851 Manatees
852 Manta ray
853 Mandarin
854 Maned wolf
855 Mange
856 Mangrove
857 Mandrill
858 Mantis
859 Man-of-war
860 Manticore

Quiz 86 (page 34)

861 Order
862 Its horns
863 Grooming
864 Herpetology
865 Sergey Prokofiev
866 Birds
867 Dogs
868 Gaur
869 Vegetation
870 They have claws

Quiz 87 (page 35)

871 Deer
872 Bear
873 Dog
874 Raccoon
875 Wallaby
876 Hare
877 Wild cat
878 Grebe
879 Duck
880 Crow

Quiz 88 (page 36)

881 Fawn
882 Pup
883 Kitten
884 Lamb
885 Leatherjacket
886 Joey
887 Cygnet
888 Squab
889 Leveret
890 Cub

Quiz 89 (page 36)

891 Tiger
892 Elephant seal
893 Ostrich
894 Bird-eating spider
895 Grey kangaroo
896 Basking shark
897 Japanese spider crab
898 Honey badger
899 Giant anteater
900 Indri

Quiz 90 (page 36)

901 Trout
902 Reindeer
903 Eagle
904 Anaconda
905 Kodiak
906 Gosling
907 Africa
908 Orinoco
909 Polyp
910 Grayling

Quiz 91 (page 36)

911 Coyote
912 Asian elephant
913 Golden cat
914 Common zebra
915 Brown bear
916 Common dolphin
917 Brown lemming
918 Common toad
919 Bactrian camel
920 Capuchin monkey

Quiz 92 (page 37)

921 Grizzly bear
922 Flippers
923 Hoverfly
924 Pilot whale
925 Scales
926 Genet
927 Sperm whale
928 Horseshoe crab
929 Tapeworm
930 Feathers

Quiz 93 (page 37)

931 100 tonnes
932 They swam in open water
933 An *Iguanodon*
934 The Triassic Period
935 Birds
936 After
937 *Ichthyosaurus*
938 Fossilised dung
939 65 million years ago
940 *Megalosaurus*

Quiz 94 (page 37)

941 Butterflies
942 42
943 The eyes
944 A lizard
945 Primary consumers
946 Siamese fighting fish
947 Largest meat-eating dinosaur
948 Through their body surface
949 A baby shark or ray
950 The avocet

Quiz 95 (page 37)

951 *Felis sylvestris*
952 *Locusta migratoria*
953 *Lemur catta*
954 *Myrmeleon formicarius*
955 *Vipera berus*
956 *Balaenoptera musculus*
957 *Sorex minutus*
958 *Alligator mississippiensis*
959 *Musca domestica*
960 *Cervus nippon*

Quiz 96 (page 38)

961 Cancer
962 Pisces
963 Scorpio
964 Camelopardalis
965 Leo
966 Serpens
967 Lupus
968 Cygnus
969 Equuleus
970 Delphinus

Quiz 97 (page 38)

971 A bird
972 Cartilage
973 Africa
974 Culture Club
975 A lion and a tiger
976 The warthog
977 Asia
978 The Owl and the Pussy-cat
979 The harpy
980 Buffalo

Quiz 98 (page 38)

981 True
982 True
983 True
984 True
985 True
986 False
987 False
988 True
989 True
990 True

Quiz 99 (page 38)

991 The dodo
992 A dolphin
993 The cow
994 The passenger pigeon
995 An endangered species
996 Tasmanian tiger or Tasmanian wolf
997 The zebra
998 Cuba
999 All of them
1000 The same one

Question sheet

Quiz Number	Quiz Title

Questions	Answers
1	1
2	2
3	3
4	4
5	5
6	6
7	7
8	8
9	9
10	10

Answer sheet

Name

Quiz Number	Quiz Title

Answers

1

2

3

4

5

6

7

8

9

10

Total score

Abbreviations:
T = top; M = middle; B = bottom;
L = left; R = right

Front cover image: Nature Picture Library/Richard du Toit.
Back cover image: Corbis

1 Nature Picture Library/John Cancalosi. **2–3** DRK Photo/John Cancalosi. **4–5** Digital Vision. **6** Trevor Boyer/from *Reader's Digest Nature Lover's Library: Field Guide To The Birds Of Britain,* published by The Reader's Digest Association Limited, London, 1997, MR. **13** Top to bottom: DRK Photo/ Wayne Lankinen, 1; DRK Photo/ John Cancalosi, 5; PhotoDisc, 2, 3, 4, 6–10. **21** Digital Vision. **25** Matthew White. **31** Digital Vision, 1–10; Roy Williams, 6. **35** Matthew White. **40** Digital Vision, ML. **40–41** Nature Picture Library/Mike Wilkes. **41** Nature Picture Library/Francois Savigny, TR; Nature Picture Library/Avi Klapfer/ Rotman, MR; Nature Picture Library/ Hans Christoph Kappel, BR. **42–43** Digital Vision. **43** Mick Loates/from *Reader's Digest Nature Lover's Library: Field Guide To The Water Life Of Britain,* published by The Reader's Digest Association Limited, London, 1985, M; Trevor Boyer/ from *Reader's Digest Nature Lover's Library: Field Guide To The Birds Of Britain,* published by The Reader's Digest Association Limited, London, 1997, MR; Bradbury and Williams, B. **44** Nature Picture Library/Martha Holmes, L; Oxford Scientific Films/Clive Bromhall, R. **45** Nature Picture Library/Anup Shah, ML; DRK Photo/Kennan Ward, MR; DRK Photo/Michael Fogden, TL; Auscape/ Jean–Paul Ferrero. **46** Corbis ML, B. **47** Bruce Coleman Collection/ Jane Burton, T; Auscape/Joe McDonald, BL, Digital Vision, BR. **48** DRK Photo/Stanley Breeden. **48–49** DRK Photo/Kennan Ward. **49** DRK Photo/Michael Fogden. **50** Digital Vision. **50–51** Oxford Scientific Films/Robin Bush. **51** DRK Photo/Anup Shah. **52** Nature Picture Library/Peter Scoone, TL; AntBits, TR. **52–53** DRK Photo/Stephen J. Krasemann. **53** Nature Picture Library/Barry Britton, TL; DRK Photo/ Michael Fogden, TR. **54** Digital Vision, BL; DRK Photo/Wayne Lynch. **55** Oxford Scientific Films/Rudie Kuiter, TR; DRK Photo/Belinda Wright, BR. **56** Science Photo Library/Eye of Science, BL. **56–57** DRK Photo/Steve Wolper. **57** Digital Vision. **58** AntBits. **58–59** DRK Photo/M.C. Chamberlain. **59** DRK Photo/S. Nielson, MR; DRK Photo/ Len Rue Jr, BR. **60** Digital Vision.

60–61 DRK Photo/Anup Shah. **61** DRK Photo/C. Allan Morgan, TM; Oxford Scientific Films/Dieter and Mary Plage, MR. **62–63** AntBits; Evolution Ribbon by Matthew White. **63** DRK Photo/M.C. Chamberlain, TL. **64–65** AntBits; Bradbury and Williams, B. **65** The Natural History Museum, London, TR. **66–67** AntBits. **68–69** AntBits. **69** Bradbury and Williams, MR. **70** Bradbury and Williams, TL; DRK Photo/Wayne Lankinen. **71** Nature Picture Library/ Doc White, TR; Ardea London Ltd/ Don Haddon, BL; Oxford Scientific Films/Konrad Wothe, BM; Still Pictures/Fritz Polking, BR. **72** DRK Photo/John Winnie Jr, ML; DRK Photo/Tom and Pat Leeson, BR. **72–73** Auscape/ Jean–Paul Ferrero. **73** DRK Photo/Anup Shah, TM; AntBits, BR. **74–75** Background/DRK Photo/Martin Harvey. **74–75** Digital Vision. **76** DRK Photo/Michael Fogden, TL; DRK Photo/M.C. Chamberlain, BR. **76–77** Digital Vision. **77** DRK Photo/Michael Fogden, TR, M. **78** DRK Photo/Tom Brakefield, TL; Martin Woodward, BL. **78–79** DRK Photo/Fred Bruemmer. **79** Auscape/ Mark Jones, TL, AntBits, MR. **80** Nature Picture Library/Neil P. Lucas. **80–81** Digital Vision. **81** DRK Photo/Pete Oxford, TL; NHPA/Dr. Ivan Polunin, R. **82** DRK Photo/Pete Oxford. **82–83** Auscape/Mark Spencer. **83** DRK Photo/Oxford Scientific Films/ Paulo De Oliveira, TL; Nature Picture Library/Doc White, BR. **84–85** Digital Vision. **86** Auscape/Ben and Lynn Cropp. **86–87** DRK Photo/ Norbert Wu. **87** Digital Vision, TL; NASA/Visible Earth/Landsat 7/ETM+/ Bruce Hatcher and Abdulla Naseer, Dalhousie University, BR. **88** Carol Hicks/National Marine Aquarium. **88–89** Oxford Scientific Films/Rob Nunnington. **89** DRK Photo/Larry Tackett, BR. **90** Nature Picture Library/Mark and Juliet Yates, ML. **90–91** Auscape/© Hellio–Van Ingen. **91** Julian Baker, TL; Nature Picture Library/Bruce Davidson, B. **92** NHPA/ James Carmichael Jr, MR; Gerald Cubitt, B. **93** Science Photo Library/ K.H. Kjeldsen; Digital Vision, BR. **94** DRK Photo/Stephen J. Krasemann, MR; DRK Photo/James P. Rowan, TL. **94–95** DRK Photo/Pete Oxford. **96** Bradbury and Williams, MR; Wildlife Art Ltd, BL. **96–97** DRK Photo/Doug Perrine. **97** Digital Vision. **98** Julian Baker, BL; Bradbury and Williams, TL. **99** Wildlife Art Ltd, TM; DRK Photo/Norbert Wu. **100** DRK Photo/ William Leonard, ML. **101** DRK Photo/Stephen J. Krasemann, ML; DRK Photo/Michael Fogden, MR; DRK Photo/David Northcott, BL;

DRK Photo/Michael Fogden, BR. **102** Bradbury and Williams, BL. **103** Oxford Scientific Films, TL; Still Pictures/Daniel Heuclin, TR; NHPA/ Daniel Zupanc, B. **104–5** DRK Photo/ S. Nielson. **105** Oxford Scientific Films/Robert Tyrrell, TL. **106** Wildlife Art Ltd, TR; Science Photo Library/ George Bernard, MR; NHPA/Henry Ausloos, BL. **106–7** DRK Photo/ Jeremy Woodhouse. **107** DRK Photo/Wayne Lankinen, MR; Bradbury and Williams, BR. **108** Nature Picture Library/David Kjaer, ML. **108–9** DRK Photo/John Cancalosi. **109** Digital Vision, TL, BM; Robert Morton/from *Reader's Digest Nature Lover's Library: Field Guide To The Birds Of Britain,* published by The Reader's Digest Association Limited, London, 1997, BL. **110** Janet Baker, MR; AntBits, BR. **111** DRK Photo/Wayne Lynch, TL; DRK Photo/Kennan Ward. **112** Janet Baker, MR; Auscape/ Jean–Paul Ferrero, B. **112–13** Digital Vision. **113** DRK Photo/ Stanley Breeden, TR; NHPA/Dave Watts, BM. **114** DRK Photo/Michael Fogden, T. **114–15** DRK Photo/Andy Rouse. **115** Oxford Scientific Films/ Des and Jan Bartlet, TL; NHPA/ Anthony Banister, TR. **116** DRK Photo/ Michael Fogden, BR. **116–17** NHPA/Stephen Dalton. **117** DRK Photo/Pete Oxford, TL; DRK Photo/ John Cancalosi, TR; Martin Woodward, BR. **118–19** DRK Photo/ John Cancalosi. **119** Nature Picture Library/John Cancalosi, TL; Drawing by Tenniel from *Alice's Adventures In Wonderland* by Lewis Carroll, published by MacMillan London Ltd, 1972 (first published 1865)/ John Meek, BL; DRK Photo/Stephen J. Krasemann, BR. **120** DRK Photo/ John Cancalosi. **121** Oxford Scientific Films/Zig Leszozynski, TL; Bradbury and Williams, BL; Nature Picture Library, BR. **122** Digital Vision. **123** DRK Photo/Jeff Foott, TL; DRK Photo/Johnny Johnson, M, MR; DRK Photo/Wayne Lankinen, BR. **124** DRK Photo/Roger Tory Peterson, BL. **124–5** DRK Photo/Tom and Pat Leeson. **125** DRK Photo/ Doug Perrine, MR; Digital Vision, BR. **126** Oxford Scientific Films/ Mike Hill, ML; Janet Baker, MR. **127** Nature Picture Library/Staffan Widstrand, T; DRK Photo/Belinda Wright, MR; Digital Vision, BM. **128** Martin Woodward, ML. **128–9** Oxford Scientific Films/ Martyn Colbeck. **129** Wildlife Art Ltd, TL; DRK Photo/Anup Shah, TR; DRK Photo/Doug Perrine, BR. **130** Janet Baker, ML; DRK Photo/ Stephen J. Krasemann, BL. **130–1** DRK Photo/Doug Perrine. **131** DRK Photo/Pete Oxford, BL.

132 DRK Photo/Pete Oxford, BL. **133** Bradbury and Williams, TL; DRK Photo/Tom and Pat Leeson, BL; NHPA/Daniel Heuclin. **134** Julian Baker, M; Digital Vision, B. **135** Bradbury and Williams, TL; DRK Photo/Pete Oxford, R; Digital Vision, BL. **136–7** Digital Vision. **137** Bradbury and Williams, TL; Oxford Scientific Films/Dani Jeske, MM; Roy Williams, MR. **138** DRK Photo/Andy Rouse, TL. **138–9** DRK Photo/Wayne Lynch. **139** DRK Photo/David Woodfall, TL. **140** Robert Morton/ from *Reader's Digest Nature Lover's Library: Field Guide To The Animals Of Britain,* published by The Reader's Digest Association Limited, London, 1994, TR, ML, M, MR; Tim Hayward/from *Reader's Digest Nature Lover's Library: Field Guide To The Animals Of Britain,* published by The Reader's Digest Association Limited, 1994, BM; Janet Baker, BL, BR. **141** Janet Baker, TL, TR; NHPA/Gerard Lacz, BR. **142–3** Nature Picture Library/David Tipling. **143** Still Pictures/Zavier Eichaker, TR; DRK Photo/Wayne Lynch, BR. **144** DRK Photo/Stanley Breeden. **145** Roy Williams, TL; Roger Stewart, BR. **146** Still from *Babe* Universal Pictures/Photo Carolyn Jones/Ronald Grant Archives, TR; © Aardman Animations Ltd, BR. **146–7** Still from *King Kong, 1933* /Ronald Grant Archives. **147** © Hanna Barbera/Yogi and Booboo/Ronald Grant Archives, BR. **148** Illustration from *The Jungle Book* by Rudyard Kipling, MacMillan and Co Ltd, London, 1896/John Meek. **149** *Surprised! Storm in the Forest* by Henri Rousseau/© The National Gallery, London, TR; Rabbit from Frederick Ashton ballet, Beatrix Potter/Dee Conway Ballet and Dance Picture Library, ML; death centenary of Edward Lear stamp © Consignia plc, 2000, reproduced by kind permission of Consignia, all rights reserved/John Meek, MR. **150** Puma United Kingdom Ltd, BL. **150–1** Allsport/ Rick Stewart. **151** From *Early Advertising*, Dover Books, TL; Bradbury and Williams, BR. **152** DRK Photo/Marty Cordano, BL. **152–3** DRK Photo/Fred Bruemmer. **153** Oxford Scientific Films/Charles Tyler, TL.

The Animal World was published by The Reader's Digest Association Ltd, London. It was created and produced for Reader's Digest by Toucan Books Ltd, London.

Questions set by
David Bodycombe and Daniel Gilpin

Reference section written by
Daniel Gilpin

For Toucan Books:
Editor
Jane Chapman
Picture researcher
Christine Vincent
Consultant
Mike Clark
Proofreader
Ken Vickery
Indexer
Dorothy Frame
Design
Bradbury and Williams

For Reader's Digest:
Project editor
Christine Noble
Project art editor
Jane McKenna
Pre-press accounts manager
Penny Grose
Editorial assistant
Katharine Swire

Reader's Digest, General Books:
Editorial director
Cortina Butler
Art director
Nick Clark

Colour origination
Colour Systems Ltd, London

Printed and bound
in Europe by Arvato, Iberia

First edition Copyright © 2002

The Reader's Digest Association Ltd,
11 Westferry Circus,
Canary Wharf,
London E14 4HE
www.readersdigest.co.uk

Reprinted with amendments 2003

We are committed to both the quality of our products and the service we provide to our customers. We value your comments, so please feel free to contact us on 08705 113366 or via our website at
www.readersdigest.co.uk

If you have any comments or suggestions about the content of our books, you can email us at
gbeditorial@readersdigest.co.uk

CONCEPT CODE: UK0095/G/S
BOOK CODE: 625-001-02
ISBN: 0 276 42714 9
ORACLE: 335500001H.00.24